That Makes Sense

Bite-sized resilience insights to lift your day

Amit Sood, MD

ISBN: 978-1-7347377-4-5

Disclaimer
The information in this book is not intended to substitute a health care provider's advice or medical care. Please consult your physician or other health care provider if you are experiencing any symptoms or have questions pertaining to the information contained in this book.

TO EVERY KIND PERSON.

YOU ARE THE SALT OF THE EARTH.

CONTENTS

	Introduction	6
Weeks 1-2	Never Give Up	8
Weeks 3-4	Have Impeccable Values	24
Weeks 5-6	Give Your Best	40
Weeks 7-8	Be Kind	58
Weeks 9-10	Live with Dignity	73
Weeks 11-12	Be Humble	89
Weeks 13-14	Serve the Underprivileged	105
Weeks 15-16	Dream Big	121
Weeks 17-18	Live with Courage	139
Weeks 19-20	Be Patient	159
Weeks 21-22	Believe in Yourself	179
Weeks 23-24	Help Others	200
	Acknowledgements	223
	Additional Resources	224
	About the Author	225

Introduction

Think about the last time you said, "That makes sense." Often that happens when a thought, an experience, or an idea aligns with your values. Also, when you find something reasonable, practical, and wise, or learn a sensible way of approaching life. In this book, I share some of those moments from my life.

Now, it isn't necessary that everything that makes sense to me should also make sense to you. That's why I have provided a "That makes sense" box on each page in the lower-left corner. If the insight on the page resonates with you, please check that box. Consider revisiting your selected insights at future times and think about them some more. Please discard those insights that remain unchecked after your first read.

The insights and information you collect in your life fills two buckets—contextual knowledge and timeless wisdom. Contextual knowledge changes with time. The details of booking an airline ticket, paying insurance premium, or filling gas in your car are contextual knowledge. This knowledge helps you live and succeed in the world.

Unlike contextual knowledge, timeless wisdom stays relevant and unchanged for a very long time. Aligning your short-term actions with your life's purpose, finding ways to remain kind, keeping the hope even when things aren't going your way—are perspectives that were as relevant a thousand years ago as they are today. Timeless wisdom helps you grow emotionally, socially, and spiritually. In this book, I have strived to capture timeless wisdom through simple daily experiences.

This book's audio accompaniment is the Year of Healing Program that I have offered throughout 2021 to bring courage, hope, and a healing perspective to many of us who may not have found a day's respite from the constant barrage of negative news.

The insights in this book are organized around 12 resilience luminaries who I spotlight through the book. They are Helen Keller, Mahatma Gandhi, Marie Curie, Abraham Lincoln, Rosa Parks, Alexander Fleming, Mother Teresa, Martin Luther King Jr., Eleanor Roosevelt, Nelson Mandela, Joan of Arc, and Harriet Tubman. Their images, half-page descriptions, and quotes are the same that I provided in the book *2021: Your Year of Healing*.

The coming months and years promise to keep challenging our peace, relationships, and grit. But giving up on hope, courage, and love isn't an option. Our children depend on us all keeping it together and handing them a healthy and hope-filled planet. Let's rise together to meet that challenge and build a world that loves your child as much as you do.

I pray peace, health, and love touch every part of your life.

WEEKS 1-2

Theme: Never give up
Inspiring figure: Helen Keller

Helen Keller graduated Phi Beta Kappa, wrote 12 books, won the Presidential Medal of Freedom, and was inducted into the National Women's Hall of Fame. All this was after losing vision and hearing at 19 months of age. Her life was strongly influenced by Anne Sullivan, Keller's companion, teacher, friend, and her source of light for nearly 50 years, helping Keller overcome her physical limitations.

Here are three of Helen Keller's most inspiring quotes:

"Although the world is full of suffering, it is also full of the overcoming of it."

"The best and most beautiful things in the world cannot be seen or even touched - they must be felt with the heart."

"Alone we can do so little; together we can do so much."

Day 1

Recognize that a lot isn't in your control. You can't stop the snow, but you can open the umbrella.

Minnesotans celebrate the first snow and the seventh, but not when it snows on the 4th of July.

Recently, my goldendoodle puppy, Simba taught me an important lesson about going with the flow. I was worried Simba won't find enough grass in deep winter. From shoveling a small patch in the yard to getting artificial grass—I weighed many different options. But when it snowed, Simba just marched into the white landscape, ran around, and loved getting wet.

Snow in Minnesota, heat in Arizona, dust storms in the Sahara are inevitable. You can't change the weather. But your mind has the choice to accept the extremes if you live at one of these places. That's choosing wisely.

Acceptance doesn't mean I love the dust storm. Accept means I won't fight a psychological battle with the storm. Instead, I will save my energy to do what I can to stay safe and savor other aspects of life.

Acceptance helps you transcend your limitations, even personal disabilities, so you turn them into strengths, transforming your life and lifting others. That's the legacy of Helen Keller.

Think of a few uncontrollable aspects of your life that you are willing to accept today.

☐

Day 2

Every person is resilient in a unique way. Ask not if I am resilient; ask, how am I resilient?

Spring paints the landscape green but also invites creepy crawly creatures. One person who is phenomenally busy in every town during the spring is the bug man. A bug man is your lifesaver if you don't particularly admire wasps, spiders, and fire ants. The bug man is very comfortable with the bugs. But when it comes to medical stuff, he isn't as savvy.

Richa, my wife, in her previous job, worked as a GYN surgeon. She was very comfortable with stitches and surgeries, but if there were a mouse in the house, she would rather be on another floor. Both the bug man and Richa are strong in their unique way.

Think today about your unique strengths. What makes you special?

Are you flexible about your preferences? Can you quickly find the good in a difficult situation? Are you very creative? Are you great with numbers?

Aligning your daily work with your strengths is a recipe for success. Also, sometimes, focusing on your strengths is a great first step to start working on your weaknesses.

So, spend a little time thinking about your unique strengths today to grow them even more.

Day 3

Just as trees grow their branches toward the sun, spend more time with the people who are your source of light.

Sunlight seems like an abundant, infinite resource, but not in the thick forests. Competition for sunlight is one of the strongest factors shaping forest architecture. Trees have adapted by learning to bend toward the light. But is that what our mind does?

Let's say you put your home up for sale for $200,000. You receive two bids. One person bids it at 180 while another counterbid at 210. Which bid will you take? The 210 one, isn't it?

Here is another situation. You receive two performance evaluations. One person gave you a 9, while the other gave you a 3. Which evaluation will occupy your mind as you are driving back home? Likely, it will be the one who gave you a 3.

With the selling price of the home, we take the highest bid; when it comes to the self, we focus on the lowest score. As a result, we spend more time thinking about people who we believe do not like us. We also attend more to what isn't right in our life. Let's do it differently today.

Spend more time thinking about the good people in your life. Who are these people?

Likely, they find joy in helping you. They have good energy. They help you feel worthy and treat you with kindness. Thinking about them brings a smile to your face. The more time you spend with these people, the higher your energy and the better your self-worth. Reminding yourself of what's special about these people will help you remember what's good in this world. It will help you feel you live in a kind world. Let's build and live in a good, kind world today.

Day 4

Your heart first serves blood to itself, to serve the body. Be kind to yourself to be kind to others.

The human heart beats about 100,000 times a day, pumping 2000 gallons of blood. Before sending the blood to the body, the heart keeps 5% of the blood flow for itself, or about 100 gallons a day. If the heart didn't do that, it wouldn't be able to serve the body.

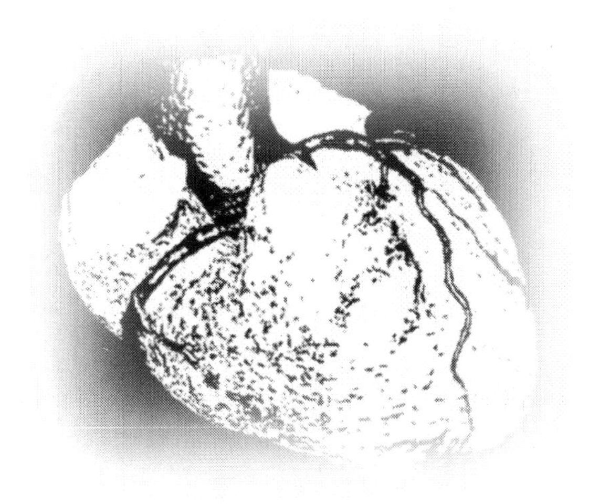

The same applies to you. Preserving your energy and being kind to yourself helps you share your energy and be kind to others.

Part of self-kindness is recognizing that every person has limitations. We are all phenomenal in many ways yet limited.

None of us can run like a cheetah, swim like a dolphin, see like an eagle, or rhyme like Dr. Seuss.

We are strong but not in every domain—no point comparing someone else's strengths with ours.

Today, think of different ways you can be kind to yourself. The entire world's kindness and love that come to you flow through you. You only receive the love you believe you deserve.

And when you choose to be kind to yourself, it becomes much easier to be kind to the world.

Day 5

Think of what made you happy before you got busy with life. It'll give you an idea of how to be happy again.

A tootsie roll, an attractive sippy cup, the company of one good friend, a video of a dog chasing his tail, a balloon, a real nice eraser—that's all toddlers need to be happier.

Perhaps, all of these made you happy when you were a toddler.

But as we get older, our thresholds change. Only something extraordinary makes us happy. We also become skilled at noticing and latching on to the negative. This attitude postpones joy.

Lower your threshold for happiness today by embracing simplicity and innocence. Enjoy the fragrance of coffee, the color of the grass, the movement of the clouds, the glow of the moon, the smile and the voice of your loved ones.

Also, try and recall a few simple things that made you happy when you were a child. It will help you steal a little extra joy from your day.

Day 6

Although shoveling doesn't make the snow disappear, it pushes the snow to the side. Clear your mind every so often to keep moving forward.

A few weeks ago, I was driving on a busy highway. As I was about to change the lane, I discovered a spider on my left shoulder.

I don't particularly like having spiders on my shoulder. But you will agree that a wobbly car while changing lanes on a busy highway would be worse.

For a few moments, I had to push the thought of the spider out of my head to focus on what was more important.

That's what we sometimes have to do during challenging moments.

Do some people dislike you for reasons best known to them?

Are you worried about the future of your medical coverage?

Are you concerned about your mom's memory lapse?

Although all of these are important, for the next hour, keep all these and other concerning thoughts to the side and lift the load of only the next one hour. Focus only on what's actionable and time sensitive. It will improve your efficiency and give you calm.

I hope you have a productive and peaceful day today.

Day 7

Here are the six key ideas we learned this week. Pick the one that makes the most sense to you for today.

- [ ] *Your life offers two kinds of challenges—the first group is within your control, and the second isn't. Stop fighting with those not in your control, so you have good energy to focus on the controllable.*
- [ ] *Recognize that every person is resilient in a unique way. Instead of asking if I am resilient, ask how I am resilient?*
- [ ] *Just as the trees bend toward the light, spend more time with the people who are the source of love and light in your life.*
- [ ] *Your heart serves blood to itself to serve the body. Serve kindness to the self, to be kind to the world.*
- [ ] *Embrace the simplicity and innocence you had as a child to find more joy in the world.*
- [ ] *Shovel negative thoughts to the side today to free your life's driveway. Focus on what's important, actionable, and time sensitive.*

I pray you find hope and healing today.

Day 8

The path to success isn't straight up. If today feels like a step back, consider that it may well be the safest and quickest path to climb higher.

A skilled climber who has scaled many mountains knows that you have to pause and take step backs to avoid treacherous terrains in many climbs.

Helen Keller had a rough start with her teacher Anne Sullivan. Keller would have outbursts of frustration. It took many tries until one day, Keller had a breakthrough. She figured out that the word water spelled on her hand conveyed her feeling of cool water.

If Sullivan and Keller had given up in the first few weeks, the world would have missed learning from Keller's brilliance and Sullivan's patience.

Failed projects, broken relationships, financial losses—they all hurt. Even a missed flight feels painful. But it helps to believe that these step backs may be move forwards. Often, it plays out over time.

I know two people who are alive today because they missed their flight. They were very upset when they missed their flight, only to realize two hours later, how lucky they were to be alive.

That experience changed their life. However, we often don't get to know how adversity prevented a catastrophe. It just helps to keep the faith during difficult times that someone is looking out for us.

So, think of a few ways recent adversity or a step back may have helped you. It will empower you to feel strong and less fearful.

☐

Day 9

Research shows although we can't change our genetic sequence, we can choose which genes are expressed. And that may be enough.

Fascinating but somewhat sad research shows that poverty adversely affects the brain's memory area called the hippocampus. Children raised in poverty have a smaller hippocampus, which often limits their academic and career progress, locking them in poverty.

Research also shows that engaged and loving parenting can completely reverse the adverse effects of poverty on the hippocampus, brightening the child's future. These beneficial effects occur through a change in gene expression.

We all have the same 20,000 genes. Within this bounty that you and I share, nature creates variations in two ways –

1. We have different versions of the same genes, and
2. We differ in which genes are expressed.

The choices you make strongly influence your genetic expression. So, your genes are like a menu at a restaurant. You get to choose the dishes you order.

A healthy diet, exercise, nurturing relationships, hope, meaning, connection, discipline, courage, commitment to kindness—all of these activate healthier genes.

Pick one or more ideas from above. Add your own ideas.

Think of a few ways you can take better care of yourself today, to improve your health and choose which genes you want to be expressed. Now that's empowering, isn't it?

Day 10

Receiving entails giving, and giving entails receiving. Feel grateful for the help you received and the help you were able to provide.

I have eaten hundreds of ice creams. But the only ice cream I remember is the one I never ate. On a scorching afternoon in New Delhi, as my wife and I settled on the chairs in front of an ice cream shop, from the corner of my eyes, I saw a little boy interested in my cone. I walked over and gave him my ice cream. The memory of his gratitude-filled eyes has nourished me dozens of times.

When you share something of value, the message you tell yourself is that I have plenty. I am contributing to a purpose on the planet. That message goes deep and activates a healthy set of genes, improving your physical and mental health.

Keep in mind that you can only give when someone is willing to receive. The people who agree to receive from you are giving you the opportunity to start a process that switches on your healthier genes. What bigger gift can anyone offer to you?

So, consider making a list of the people who have helped you by agreeing to receive your help, and feel grateful for them. I hope this insight will add hundreds if not thousands to your gratitude list.

☐

Day 11

Crying helps immunity and is our way of healing. Often, the best laughs come only after the heart is emptied of tears.

I recently came across some fascinating research. In this study, researchers looked at the effect of emotions on patients with arthritis. Their conclusion: people who were easily moved to tears had fewer arthritis flares and had better immune markers.

I don't know when we started believing that expressing emotions is a sign of weakness. That stiff people, who wouldn't laugh, or cry are strong. The truth may be just the opposite.

Expressing authentic emotions is good for your health. Both laughing and crying can help you heal and make you healthier.

Your emotional expressions help others too. Your happiness increases your loved ones and friends' happiness. Your tears show that you care.

Now it's important to laugh with and not laugh at. Also, cry because you care, not because you spot a weed in your yard.

Here is an idea. Think of a few people you know who are easily moved to tears. Most likely, you will agree that they are kind, good people.

So, don't feel bad about your authentic emotional expressions. Such expressions show your kindness to yourself and others and are healthy for you and the people you serve and love.

Day 12

Waiting for a phenomenal achievement to feel grateful could be a very long wait. Fill your day with gratitude for the ordinary and simple.

When I look back on the last ten years, most of my achievements have been small, almost inconsequential—a paper published, a research grant approved, an academic promotion, and such.

Perhaps, for most of us, extraordinary achievements are only an occasional occurrence.

But the small joys and successes happen a lot.

A cup of coffee precisely to your taste, quality time with friends and loved ones, a good jog, a rejuvenating shower, a perfect parking spot, and more.

Choose to be grateful for the ordinary and simple because it indeed is extraordinary and precious. Often, we realize the value of the ordinary only when it isn't accessible anymore.

Do not let that happen to you.

Think of a few simple things that you would have barely noticed, but you are grateful for today. Feel blessed to have these simple pleasures in your life. The more blessed you feel, the more blessed you will feel. It's that simple.

☐

Day 13

Spills happen. Your two best choices are: First, clean up and then have a good laugh. Or, first, have a good laugh and then clean up!

A few years ago, I was in the bedroom when I heard a loud thud in the living room. I rushed to see what happened. My grandma had fallen on the floor.

The moment our eyes met, she started laughing. I was startled but relieved. She wasn't in pain and thus had no broken bones. To her, falling without breaking a bone was an adventure, like going on a giant roller coaster.

My grandma taught me that being able to laugh amidst daily annoyances—slips, spills, minor losses—can convert those annoyances into happier moments.

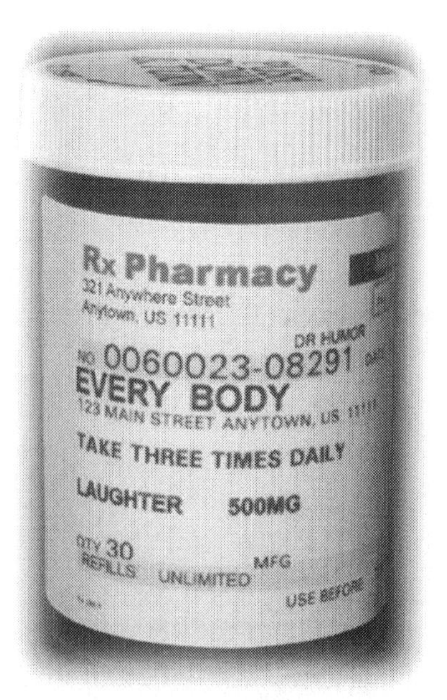

Laughter and health go together. Laughter improves your anti-viral immunity and physical health, decreases pain, and enhances social connections. When you laugh, you send the message, "I like you. I trust you. I am willing to play with you."

So, let go of some of your past "spills" and find humor in them to the extent you can. That will give you better control of your mind, infuse extra joy, and even decrease the number of future spills.

☐

Day 14

Here are the six key ideas we learned this week. Pick the one that makes the most sense to you for today.

- [ ] *Recognize that in any climb step backs are inevitable. In fact, step backs offer the safest and quickest route to the top.*
- [ ] *Taking care of your health not only improves your present wellbeing but also materially changes your genetic expression, setting you up for lasting positive health.*
- [ ] *People who allow you to help them are truly assisting every aspect of your life. Feel grateful to those who willingly accept your help.*
- [ ] *Both crying and laughing can help your immunity. Your happiness increases your loved ones and friends' happiness. Your tears show that you care.*
- [ ] *Simple things happen many times during the day, while phenomenal achievements are rare. If you choose to be grateful for the simple and ordinary, that will gift you many moments of joy on otherwise "ordinary" days.*
- [ ] *Try to find humor in everyday annoyances to convert those into positive moments.*

I pray you find hope and healing today.

WEEKS 3-4

Theme: Have impeccable values; stick to your ideals
Inspiring figure: Mahatma Gandhi

A modestly successful lawyer, moved by his personal insult and the plight of those around him, launched the most powerful non-violent movement the world has ever seen. His work brought freedom to India and inspired several non-violent and civil rights movements across the globe.

Here are three of Gandhi's most inspiring quotes:

"Be the change that you wish to see in the world."

"Live as if you were to die tomorrow. Learn as if you were to live forever."

"An eye for an eye will only make the whole world blind."

Day 15

Recognize that the people who you find annoying often have constraints that you don't know and may never know.

A friend of mine stopped answering her texts. She didn't even respond when I asked her about a loved one's urgent medical issue. I was unhappy with her. I thought she didn't care about me anymore.

A few weeks later, I came to know that she had closed herself from the world because she was diagnosed with advanced cancer. I felt small at judging her.

Another situation. A close loved one is very sensitive to critique, even when he clearly is wrong and has messed up. Nevertheless, he loves to point out my slightest mistake. This used to annoy me to the core until I realized that he had a very adverse childhood, and probably his behavior is his subconscious effort to protect his self-worth.

I am sure you have a few such annoying people in your life.

Here is what I suggest. It may help to consider that most people you find annoying have one or more constraints. And they may feel too vulnerable to share their constraints with you.

When you assume that others are stuck in a difficult situation and are not intentionally trying to be difficult, you become kind to them and yourself.

Today, think of a few good reasons why someone annoying may be justified from within his perspective. If you can't think of a good cause, then assume that such a reason exists. When you connect with that person, use compassion before judgment. It will help you nurture a better relationship with the world and the self.

Day 16

Remembering a good deed is as joyous the tenth time as it is the first time. Seed future happiness by doing something good today.

Research shows that for our brain, imagination is reality. Thinking about the past good deeds or doing something good activates very similar brain areas. Even planning a good activity feels uplifting. That's the reason sometimes the most enjoyable part of a worthy project is its planning.

Today, make a list of three of your most impactful kind actions. Did you go out of the way to connect with someone who was struggling, helped a stranded motorist, gave your seat to a senior citizen, shared your food with someone hungry,

helped a colleague with a project, held the door a little longer for a stranger.

Making this list will remind you that you are a good person.

Such reminders not only provide a little extra lift to your day, but they also set you up for future acts of kindness, putting you in an upward spiral of life.

Day 17

During a difficult moment, it helps to ask what kind of a story I wish to tell in the future about how I handled this moment.

A couple of men were playing baseball in their neighborhood. In the middle of the game, the ball went past the fence into a person's yard. One of the men, let's call him Bill, who had recently attended the SMART resilience workshop, went to retrieve the ball.

The neighbor declined to give the ball back, saying, "What if the ball had hit my head. I am not giving it."

Bill, a strong muscular guy, had the urge to jump the fence, punch the guy, and retrieve the ball.

But he paused. He heard himself say, "I understand, sir. I wish you well." And walked away.

Bill could have put himself and the neighbor in great trouble if he had jumped the fence and got into a brawl.

Such difficult moments that hijack our Amygdala (the stress center of our brain) can go in two directions. Either they seed regrets of a lifetime or become moments of glory.

Often, it helps to ask— "What kind of a story I wish to tell in the future about how I handled this moment?"

So, think of the actions you will be proud of, not what your adrenaline wants you to do right away.

Put this idea to use if you are dealing with a present difficult situation. Think of a few ways you can handle it with grace. You will be proud of yourself as you look back at life.

☐ 

Day 18

Do not judge yourself if you were slow and unproductive today. Some days are like that. The important thing is you kept going.

Some days I wake up with lots of energy. Other days I would rather hide beneath my blanket until the sun has completed half its journey.

Similarly, some days everything falls into place. Other days, most of the traffic lights show their red face to me.

That's just the nature of the days…and life. You can't be perfectly productive every single day.

In fact, sometimes, it helps you to go slow. Tardy progress gives you time to think, savor, and reset if that's what you desire.

Think of some good reasons why every day cannot be phenomenally productive, and it's OK to be non-productive at times.

The important thing is, however slow, you adhered to your values and kept going. Holding on to your values, particularly during challenging times, is what keeps you on track in your journey to your north star.

Day 19

Ordinary activity performed with extraordinary presence becomes extraordinary. Consider transforming an ordinary experience today.

Most of my day is one ordinary activity after another. Getting ready in the morning, meetings, presentations, writing, eating, chatting, emails, and more. I assume that's how it will be for most of my life.

But I find that my moments go better on days I immerse myself in ordinary activities with greater intentionality and deeper presence.

When I choose to feel the water during the shower in the morning instead of rushing through it, I feel more rejuvenated.

When I start my meetings feeling grateful for the people in front of me and send them a silent good wish, my meetings become more enjoyable and productive.

When I think of everyone who collaborated to bring food to my table during the meals, I relish what I eat a little more.

When I remember that every good person in my life isn't there by accident, they are choosing to be with me, I find them extra special. I feel grateful, happy, content, and worthy, thinking this thought.

Each of these approaches converts the ordinary transactional activity into a slightly more uplifting moment.

Try this today. Engage with a few simple daily experiences assuming they are extra special. When you assume they are special, they indeed will become more engaging and enjoyable.

Day 20

A lot may have happened today. How you feel depends on what you ignore and what you look with a magnifying glass.

That was a rough week. It started with finding mouse droppings in the basement. Then my back started acting up, followed by my daughter having a high-grade fever for several days. We took her to the ER. She had a raging infection and was dehydrated. After multiple attempts, they were able to get an IV. It took several days before she recovered. As we left the hospital, we had another concern. This infection wasn't a one-and-done deal. It could recur.

While that concern lingered, we had a lot to be grateful for; the timely diagnosis, effective antibiotics, health insurance, a healthy immune system. My back also got better, and we were able to trap the mouse.

As we drove back home from the hospital, we chose to focus on what went right within what went wrong. Our focus helped us remain strong and hopeful. It also taught us that even during a difficult moment, gratitude can help us.

Most days, a few things go right, and a few go wrong. You have a choice where to focus.

Today, focus on and magnify what went right. Such a focus will give you hope, courage, and inspiration.

☐

Day 21

Here are the six key ideas we learned this week. Pick the one that makes the most sense to you for today.

- ☐ *Instead of getting mad at someone annoying, think of a few good reasons why that person may be justified from within her or his perspective.*
- ☐ *Think of a few of your past good deeds to feel more worthy and happy and keep doing good.*
- ☐ *When going through a difficult moment, ask how you want to remember this moment. Do you want to remember that you lashed out at someone who was wrong, or you chose to be kind and offered that person an opportunity to improve? In general, you will create more positive memories if you choose to be kind.*
- ☐ *Recognize and accept that not every day can be equally productive, and sometimes, a slow unproductive day is precisely what your mind needs.*
- ☐ *Engage with a few simple daily experiences assuming that they are extra special. Your experience depends as much on your attitude and presence as it does on the event's details.*
- ☐ *Think about the top five things that went right today. How you feel depends on what you ignore and what you look with a magnifying glass.*

I pray you find hope and healing today.

Day 22

Do not peg your self-worth on your paycheck. Peg your self-worth on the meaning you fulfill and the values you live by.

Mahatma Gandhi was a shy person who didn't look physically domineering. But look at what he accomplished. The global non-violent and civil rights movements that he inspired have helped billions of lives.

Yet, his net worth at one time was estimated to be Rupees 1000 that translates to about 14 dollars.

Some of the hardest working, brilliant, and patriotic people aren't compensated or respected proportionate to the value they bring, while many professionals are adored and reap millions despite adding little to no value to the world.

Clearly, our society has a disconnect between the meaning we fulfill and the dollar rewards it provides. While you and I cannot change that disconnect today, we can choose not to let that disconnect block our pursuits. If we did that, then we would give the unkind elements in the world a second victory.

Instead of feeling disappointed by the meagerness of material rewards, take great pride in what you do by focusing on the people you help and the purpose you fulfill. Let your purpose guide your self-worth because that indeed is the true value of your contribution to the world.

Thank you for what you do.

Day 23

Best not to multitask when spending time with others; partial presence feels worse than absence.

After a long and challenging day, I was once talking to a physician colleague about a young patient with unrelenting back pain.

I said, "I saw this young man with severe mid-back pain."

"Hum," he said.

"We got an X-ray that didn't show anything. So, we got an MRI."

"That's great," he said.

I continued, "The MRI showed that the patient has extensive cancerous deposits."

"That's great," he said again.

Well, that wasn't the response I was expecting.

Clearly, he wasn't listening.

I feel missing a person when he is absent can be painful. But missing a person in his presence is even more painful. That leaves us with very little hope.

Try to be fully present in your conversations today. Also, commit to giving five minutes of your complete presence to a few people this week, assuming they are novel and priceless, which they indeed are.

☐ 

Day 24

Trees don't make roots the night of the storm. Build your positivity muscles, little by little, every single day.

Do you recall all the details of the book you read or the podcast you listened to six months ago? Most likely not. Mind's nature is to forget. We retain a tiny percentage (less than 10%) of what we hear in a presentation.

But perhaps you remember something you read this morning, even what you had for breakfast.

That's the advantage of recency. You remember the recent details.

Several studies show that students reminded of their values the same day behave with much more integrity compared to students who took an intensive course in values a few months prior.

So, one of the best ways to change your life's direction is to remind yourself of your core values, little by little, every single day.

That's one reason I feel passionate about your participation in an ongoing program that connects with you every day and reminds you of how good you are and can be.

For now, think about, write, and then meditate on three core values that guide your personal and professional life. Align your day with one of these values. I hope this simple exercise will reset your mind and uplift your day.

Day 25

We focus on and believe the criticisms much more than the compliments. Do not discount the compliments that come your way.

Like most human beings, I would rather be praised than criticized.

Every critique of my presentation—he needs to enunciate better, speaks too fast, has too many ideas jumbled together—registers deep in my psyche.

What I don't see is that for every two-star review of my book, there are perhaps ten five-star reviews. For every critique of my presentation, many share that they were truly moved.

My mind tends to dwell on the negative and not let go of hurts and insults. Perhaps, the same applies to you. That's part of our negativity bias. In a sense, it's the same as sleeping on a bed of flowers but mostly feeling the one thorn sticking into the skin. We can't help it.

While we don't have a choice with the thorn because the sensory system is designed to prioritize pain, we do have a choice with the critique. You can choose to wear an emotional armor that doesn't let the thorns of insults penetrate you but is porous to the fragrance of the accolade petals that nourish you.

Do not dilute the good with the not-so-good. Instead, let the good dominate the bad.

For today, recall a few good words you have heard about yourself. They are an accurate reflection of who you indeed are.

☐ 

Day 26

If you can't forgive yet, just keep the intent to forgive. That may be enough to free your mind at this moment.

Forgiveness can be difficult and maybe a tall order when you have been egregiously hurt. But dozens of research studies show that forgiveness helps with emotional, physical, and social wellbeing. Here is one approach I take.

I categorize forgiveness (and hurts) into three types.

The first group includes innocent hurts. A toddler grazing your cheek, a waiter accidentally spilling water on you, someone mistakenly dialing a wrong number and waking you up from a nap—these are unintentional mistakes best forgiven.

We will come to the second group in a minute. The third group of hurts is the vicious one. Intentionally harming innocent children, abusing someone vulnerable, driving under the influence, and hitting someone—I find these very difficult to forgive. Let's not even go there and focus for now on the second group of hurts.

Your partner forgot your birthday, you heard someone badmouthing you at a meeting, a loved one didn't like the dish you prepared at a party, and let everyone know—these are reasonable reasons to be upset. But sometimes, it helps to ask if the cost of being upset is more than the benefit I am getting from it.

With the second group of hurts it helps to recall why you are grateful to the person who hurt you. If you feel that the hurt happened without a vicious intention, then perhaps, forgiveness might make sense.

So, consider picking a second kind of hurt today. Note a few good things about the person who annoyed you. And if you feel up to it, at least keep the intent to forgive for now, even if you aren't ready to forgive. It will lower the cognitive and emotional load your mind has to carry in this moment.

Day 27

Carefully choose the gadgets you allow in your life. Leverage technology to enhance and not replace your presence.

I remember my family's first refrigerator. It brought delight to our taste buds. The refrigerator also expanded the variety of foods we could eat. We had access to fresh vegetables, cold water, and a predictable supply of milk.

A few years later, a television decorated our living room. First, it was black and white TV with two channels. Then came the color TV. The channels multiplied from 2 to 20 to 2000.

The same transformation happened to cell phones. From a simple flip phone to a smartphone that is now loaded with apps and social media accounts that can keep me occupied for the rest of my life.

Gadgets are of two kinds—those that sit there to help us and those that pull our attention. Increasingly, innovators are developing gadgets that take over our life. These technologies sneak into our life while we are looking elsewhere.

I believe the purpose of technology is to do things faster, better, and with greater comfort, so we can save time for each other. Technology that steals our time from each other makes little sense. Very likely, one or more of these technologies have trespassed into your life.

Today, take count of your engagement with technology and gadgets and consider removing one such distraction from your life that is usurping your time from your friends and loved ones. You will then have taken one step to intelligently leverage technology to help you instead of the gadgets and gizmos ruling over your life.

Day 28

Here are the six key ideas we learned this week. Pick the one that makes the most sense to you for today.

- ☐ *Anchor your self-worth in the meaning you fulfill and the values you embody and not your material net worth.*
- ☐ *Avoid multitasking when spending time with people; partial presence sometimes feels worse than absence.*
- ☐ *Every single day spend a little time building your positivity muscles. Trees don't sit all year round doing nothing and start making roots only on the night of the storm.*
- ☐ *Know that the human brain focuses on and believes the criticisms much more than the compliments. Choose not to discount the compliments, however small, that are coming your way today.*
- ☐ *If you have been hurt and can't forgive just yet, keep the intent to forgive particularly for the hurts that you believe happened without a bad intention.*
- ☐ *Decrease or increase the use of one gadget or technology from your life to improve your connections with loved ones and friends.*

I pray you find hope and healing today.

WEEKS 5-6

Theme: Give your best, be generous
Inspiring figure: Marie Curie

Growing up with few resources, partly because of her family's patriotic engagements, Marie Curie was the first woman to become a Professor at the University of Paris and the first person (and woman) to win the Nobel Prize in two fields, Physics and Chemistry. A philanthropist, she donated much of her Nobel Prize money and chose not to patent radium isolation so others could freely use it.

Here are three of Curie's most inspiring quotes:

"Nothing in life is to be feared. It is only to be understood."

"First principle: never to let one's self be beaten down by persons or by events."

"Radium is not to enrich anyone. It is an element; it is for all people"

Day 29

The meaning that drives you is more powerful than the fears that hold you.

Marie Curie had many excuses to give up on her efforts.

She didn't have the funding, had to work extra hours, and experienced bias in research. The geopolitical situation around her wasn't stable. She was raising two daughters and, in the middle of it all, lost the love of her life, her husband and her partner in research, Pierre Curie, in a freak accident.

But Curie remained undeterred. Perhaps her work was her therapy. The meaning behind her work was much more powerful than the setbacks or fears that held her. She not only transformed her field but had such tremendous influence on her family that Irene, one of her daughters, herself won a Nobel prize.

Your meaning could be related to what you build, who you become, or your faith. Importantly, your meaning relates to the people you serve and love—your friends, loved ones, colleagues, neighbors, clients, and others.

Take a moment today and think of the different ways you are a blessing to this world. You can start by thinking about the people you are serving and loving through all you do. The awareness of your purpose might provide a lift to your day.

Day 30

Birds with asymmetric feathers are the ones that fly. Perhaps, your day's asymmetries, even though annoying, are providing you a lift.

We love symmetry. The beauty of the Taj Mahal is partly in its extraordinary symmetry. We find symmetrical faces more attractive.

Even insects prefer symmetry. A more symmetric-looking bug is more likely to find a mate.

But there are times symmetry doesn't help. For example, symmetric feathers do not provide the lift needed for flying. Birds like Emus and Ostriches
that can't fly have symmetric feathers, while the feathers of your Robin or Parakeet are asymmetric.

Some experiences and people bring asymmetry and discomfort in our life. But it helps to consider that perhaps, over the long term, they are the ones
providing us a lift—emotional and spiritual.

With the above perspective, stretch your imagination, and think of how a few of your annoying experiences could be ultimately helpful. Your mindset will help you better handle those annoyances.

Day 31

Our sun boils and freezes many planets before getting it just right. Expect your many efforts will fail before you get it just right.

The 8 minutes and 20 seconds it takes the light and infrared waves to reach the earth from the sun is just the optimal amount of time and distance to cool from a burning 9940 degrees Fahrenheit at the solar surface to a balmy 70 degrees. If it took 10 seconds longer, we would chill into Antarctica; 10 seconds shorter, the entire planet would be a Death Valley.

Think of how long it took you to learn biking. Perhaps you started with a tricycle, then trainer wheels, next to a small bike with your mom or dad holding the bike. With time, you developed finesse and confidence and now can bike independently.

Most phenomenal achievements take time, a lot of time.

Instead of focusing on your academic B and C grades, today, recognize all the aspects of life in which you are scoring an A+.

Also, recognize all the hard work and sacrifices you had to make and the obstacles you overcame to be where you are. This recognition will help you feel stronger and become a little kinder to yourself.

☐

Day 32

Hope doesn't mean it won't get dark. Hope means no matter how dark the night, the sun will appear. It always has and always will.

Hope is your expectation of a better tomorrow. Hope gives you the reason to get out of your bed each morning. Hope keeps the faith that the traffic jam will clear, the baby will grow out of diapers, and the boring meeting will come to an end. The more hopeful you are, the better your physical and emotional health and the closer your relationships. Research shows the hopeful take better care of themselves and even live longer.

Here is a hopeful thought. Hope isn't a fixed trait. You can develop the hope habit. A few ways you can increase your hope are:

· Take better care of your physical health. The healthier you are, the more hopeful you feel.

· Remember the obstacles you have already overcome. Thinking of your strengths fills you with hope.

· Count all that is in your control at this moment. The more you feel in control, the more hopeful you become.

· Nurture faith as you feel appropriate. Faith and surrender are strong source of hope for many.

· Keep the company of positive people who spend a lot of their day helping others. Hope is infectious that you can catch from these people.

Once a student colleague of mine was worried that she might fail a test. She is a brilliant student. I asked her if she had ever failed a test in the past. She said No.

Then I asked in how many tests has she been concerned that she could fail. She said every single time.

She got the idea. That little conversation gave her some insight and hope that she would do just fine, like every previous time.

You have accomplished a lot from the time you were born. Thinking of all the obstacles you have overcome will make you feel more hopeful today.

Based on the above, think and write who and what gives you hope.

Day 33

Not all battles are worth fighting. Carefully choose which battles are worthy of your time and which ones are best bypassed.

I was once talking to a colleague who has raised two children.

"Any tips. Anything you regret," I asked.

"I should have let my son dye his hair pink when he wanted that," she said.

What I heard her say was that she wished she was a little kinder.

I feel it's best to pick your battles. Sometimes the challenges we pick aren't worth fighting and are very expensive. They deplete the trust and love in our relationships.

Within reason, the more you can honor others' preferences, the better. It helps them feel valued, a strong nourishment for your relationships.

One of the crucial times to remember kindness is while driving. I have seen many perfectly rational people become angry and violent behind the wheels. Did you get annoyed with someone who cut you off on the road, honked at you, showed the middle finger, or said the f word? If yes, then while you may be justified in your anger, that person went his merry way but left you inflamed.

For someone getting angry at you, it helps to remember that someone angry is in a more miserable situation than you are. It might be best to have compassion for their situation and perhaps for the ignorance.

Consider asking yourself today: which annoyances am I okay with letting go because they aren't worth my time?

The annoyances bypassed will save you time to focus on your life's purpose.

Day 34

Feel extra gratitude and love for all the animals in your life today. Life's spark is precious in every being.

Interesting research shows that having a pet at home (particularly dogs and cats) improves the quality of your sleep, your mood, and even your immunity. They lower your stress level, enhance your physical activity, and might prevent a stroke. I know I have spent more time outdoors and made many more neighborhood friends since my dog Simba came into our life.

I am sure you have heard of stories where dogs have acted with courage and intellect in an emergency and saved an owner's life.

Animals do so much to support and help us—cows, cats, ducks, sheep, dogs, elephants, goats, pigs, horses, chicken—all of them. Even the rodents have served us well. Many modern drugs wouldn't be around if the guinea pigs didn't act as guinea pigs.

Today, make a list of all the animals in your life and with fondness think about them.

It might bring a smile to your face and connect you with the animals even deeper.

☐

Day 35

Here are the six key ideas we learned this week. Pick the one that makes the most sense to you for today.

- ☐ *Focus less on your fears and more on your meaning. The meaning that drives you is more powerful than the fears that hold you.*
- ☐ *Recognize that your day's asymmetries, even though annoying, are providing you a lift. Birds with asymmetric feathers are the ones that fly.*
- ☐ *Just as our sun boils and freezes many planets before getting it just right, expect your many efforts will fail before you get it just right.*
- ☐ *Keep your hopes alive. Hope doesn't mean it won't get dark. Hope means no matter how dark the night, the sun will appear. It always has and always will.*
- ☐ *Remember that not all battles are worth fighting. Carefully choose which battles are worthy of your time and which ones are best bypassed.*
- ☐ *Life's spark is precious in every being. Feel extra gratitude and love for all the animals in your life to feel better connected with them.*

I pray you find hope and healing today.

Day 36

Now more than ever, nurture a healthier immune system through a nourishing diet, moderate exercise, adequate sleep, and connecting with loved ones and friends.

A robust immune system is always of great importance, but it has assumed even greater importance now.

Based on a large body of research, here are eight ideas that can help your immune system.

1. Avoid micronutrient deficiency – Micronutrients are vitamins and minerals that we need from outside sources. One out of three among us may be micronutrient deficient that hurts the immune system. A diet that emphasizes fruits and vegetables, healthy proteins, and whole grains will help boost your micronutrient level. In some instances, supplementation that provides 100% of recommended daily intake might also help.

2. Stress resilience – Decrease your cognitive and emotional load by creating a not-to-do list and limiting your worries. Be kind to the self and spend more time with the people who care about you.

3. Relationships – Try your best to assume positive intent when someone annoys you.

4. Movement – Be active and agile and avoid prolonged sitting. Take the stairs when you can.

5. Happiness – The happier you are, the stronger your immune system. A good belly laugh can boost your immunity for up to 12

hours. Add humor and laughter to lift your days.

6. Sleep – Consider sleep as a productive time that helps you rejuvenate. Avoid fear and anger before you sleep because strong negative feelings will prevent a night of deep restorative sleep.

7. Purity – Minimize the intake of pesticides, heavy metals, and other impurities in your food, air, and water. Quit smoking and use of addicting drugs and minimize alcohol intake.

8. Healthy compounds – Increase your intake of antioxidants that protect your body cells. The richest source of antioxidants is fruits and vegetables.

Pick one idea from the above list that makes the most sense to you for today. You can find more information if you wish at immuneresilience.com.

Day 37

Older trees provide shade and not fruit, and that's enough. Best to respect and value our seniors. They are the cherished treasures of our families and our world.

Depression and loneliness are common in our seniors. Often, these problems relate to a loss of meaning. Much of our meaning is anchored in work and relationships that commonly fade as we get older.

Once, a senior member in my family felt despondent that he wasn't meaningfully contributing to the home or the economy. We sat down, and I shared with him the life cycle of a tree.

A seed becomes a sapling that grows into a plant that then becomes a tree. A tree spends many years keeping the soil together, adding oxygen to the atmosphere, and producing fruits. After a lifetime of contribution, the tree stops making fruits. But it is still holding the soil together and providing shade and shelter.

"That's what you are doing," I shared with the senior member. "Your presence is a blessing to us. You do not need to produce any fruits."

It brought tears to his eyes.

I remember this thought almost every week: Best to love the living instead of waiting to praise them in a memorial service.

So, friend, think of how you can help a senior in your life feel valued and loved. Treat them with the same courtesy and grace you want to be treated when you stop contributing meaningfully to the economy.

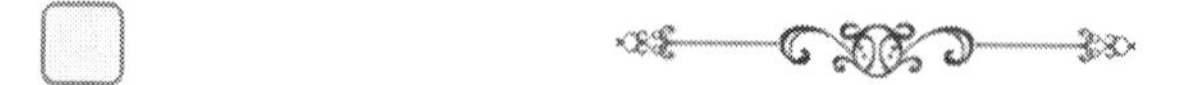

Day 38

Seeing the good in the bad isn't denying the bad. It is denying the bad from taking over your mind.

A few years ago, I was driving with my family to a small town about 100 miles from my city. It was a gorgeous day with a clear sky and bright sun—one precious day in the four weeks of summer that we get in Minnesota! Suddenly, I heard a loud bang in the back. The car became wobbly. I was in the right lane and quickly got on the shoulder. It was a burst tire.

After confirming what had happened and a few anxious seconds, we focused on the good. We were in the right lane, there was hardly any traffic, the car didn't topple since we were at 70 mph, and this was just a burst tire, nothing more.

The quick reframing helped keep our adrenaline in check.

Recognize that when you choose to see the good in the bad, you don't deny the bad. You prevent the bad from taking over your mind. Too much adrenaline disrupts your brain's thinking and problem-solving areas. You want to keep that in check.

So, consider thinking about what went right within what went wrong. It will help you preserve your energy to fix the wrong.

Day 39

Adding honey dilutes the bitterness in the tea. Similarly, adding gratitude, compassion, and meaning dilutes life's challenges, making them more bearable.

During a conversation, I was once challenged by a colleague. She said, "The world seems falling apart. How do I stay positive? Isn't that unreal?"

I agreed with her that unbridled hope and positivity would be unreal. Our minds would resent that. Since she was drinking tea at that time, I asked her, "What would you do if this tea was very bitter, and you still want to drink it?

"I would put some honey in it," she said.

"That's precisely the point. The bitter life becomes a bit more palatable by adding the honey of gratitude, compassion, and meaning."

Sensing her agreement and interest, I continued. "No need to force positivity. Just add gratitude, compassion, and meaning to your experience. That will be plenty to transform your moments, your days, perhaps even your life."

Friend, gratitude, compassion, and meaning help when the going is good. They are even more important when the going gets tough.

Try and find gratitude, compassion, and, if possible, meaning in a previous life challenge. It might help soften the pain that challenge may have caused you and free your mind to focus on this moment.

☐

Day 40

No matter what you do, your job description includes being a happiness officer at work and home, for others and yourself.

Happiness has many sources. The most powerful source of happiness comes from connections. Connections provide you identity and self-worth in two ways.

The first is through receiving. Getting love and respect helps you feel happier.

The second is through giving. When you help others feel loved, respected, and valued, through your words and actions, you feel happier.

Open yourself up to receive the love and respect already flowing toward you.

You can do this little experiment today. Assign the role of happiness officer to everyone in your home or with your friends or colleagues. Also, assign everyone one person, they will try to make happier. At the end of the experiment, you might realize that gifting others a few extra jovial moments is a powerful source of personal happiness.

I hope this little exercise will inspire you to be a happiness officer for someone each day of this week.

Day 41

We compare our weaknesses with others' strengths and their weaknesses with our strengths. This creates judgment toward others and self. Every person is strong and weak in his or her unique way.

I was once helping a colleague write a research protocol. That was when I was deep into research and could churn out a ten-page protocol in two days. After a full three months of mentoring, she was able to write one good page. I started getting frustrated. I couldn't understand why writing a research proposal would be so difficult for her. I was comparing my strength with her weakness.

It occurred to me one day that maybe this is not her thing. We had a frank conversation. She confessed to her struggles with research going back to her high school days. We found a different path for her that involved more clinical care. Success! She is one of the most effective therapists in the country.

We have this instinct to compare others' weaknesses with our strengths, thereby judging others; and our weaknesses with their strengths, thereby judging ourselves. I think it's better to assume that everyone is strong in a unique way and leveraging their strength instead of focusing on weaknesses might be the right approach to bring out the best in them.

Consider listing some of your strengths today that many people don't know, and think of how you can leverage them? Who knows it might open a new opportunity or simply a new hobby. Happy exploring!

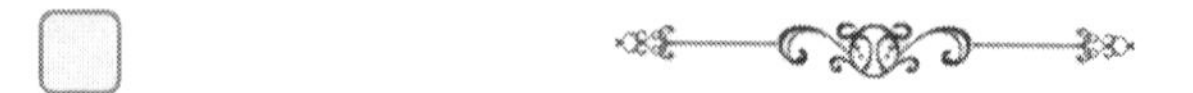

Day 42

Here are the six key ideas we learned this week. Pick the one that makes the most sense to you for today.

- ☐ *Now more than ever, nurture a healthier immune system through a nourishing diet, moderate exercise, adequate sleep, and connecting with loved ones and friends.*

- ☐ *Older trees provide shade and not fruit, and that's enough. Best to respect and value our seniors. Think of how you can help a senior in your life feel valued and loved.*

- ☐ *Seeing the good in the bad isn't denying the bad. It is denying the bad from taking over your mind. Think of what went right within something that went wrong.*

- ☐ *Adding honey dilutes the bitterness in the tea. Similarly, adding gratitude and meaning dilutes life's challenges, making them more bearable. Try and find gratitude, compassion, and, if possible, meaning in a previous life challenge.*

- ☐ *No matter what you do, your job description includes being a happiness officer, at work and home, for others and yourself. Think of how you can make others and yourself a little happier today.*

- ☐ *We compare our weaknesses with others' strengths and their weaknesses with our strengths. This creates judgment toward others and self. Every person is strong and weak in their unique way. List some of your strengths that many people don't know.*

I pray you find hope and healing today.

WEEKS 7-8

Theme: Be kind; have exceptional integrity
Inspiring figure: Abraham Lincoln

With little formal education, Abraham Lincoln self-educated himself to become a successful lawyer, rose to become a U.S. congressman, and finally the 16th President of the United States. Two of his most notable contributions were his leadership during the Civil War and his Emancipation Proclamation. He was a humble and kind person, known for his exceptional integrity.

Here are three of Lincoln's most inspiring quotes:

"Whatever you are, be a good one."

"Do I not destroy my enemies when I make them my friends?"

"Give me six hours to chop down a tree and I will spend the first four sharpening the axe."

Day 43

The path to remarkable success is invariably marked with unanticipated hurdles. Many step-backs, in reality, are move forwards.

He lost his bid for the state legislature, failed in business, lost his sweetheart, was defeated for the job of the speaker, didn't get nominated for congress, didn't get the job of land officer, was defeated for the U.S. Senate, didn't receive the vice-presidential nomination, again was defeated for the U.S. Senate, and then finally in 1861, was elected as the 16th president of the United States. That's the career trajectory of Abraham Lincoln, one of the most celebrated presidents in American history.

Just as a diamond needs polishing to shine and gold needs molding to become jewelry, we need to go through a journey that is often pockmarked with adversities to transform us. Our falls ensure that we do not take our rise for granted.

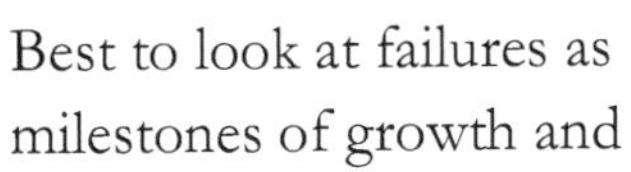

Best to look at failures as milestones of growth and step-backs as momentary reversals on a path that helps you move forward at a speed that is right for you.

So today, think of how a previous step-back could have been a move forward. Without denying the undesirability of step-backs, such a perspective accepts their inevitability, and helps you keep moving forward.

Day 44

Smile and say hello. There is a better than one in two chance that the person in front of you feels vulnerable and lonely.

I remember my struggles when I first came to the U.S. over 25 years ago. I struggled with language, didn't know how to work the ATMs, or drive in the left lane. I felt awkward, misfit. Within a few days of arriving, I started working long hours as an intern in an inner-city hospital. Several times during a week, we would work 30 hours nonstop.

In those difficult days, a smile from someone, anyone, felt like an oasis. Small talk would soothe me for hours.

I struggled in silence, which I believe is the lived experience of many. A patient once said to me, "I am the only one hurting. Everyone in the lobby seems OK."

"If every patient in the lobby feels the same, then who isn't struggling," I thought.

It's fair to assume that every person around you is struggling in a unique way, particularly in the current times. This assumption will make you kinder.

So, think of one or more moments during the day when you can be a little kinder and more engaged. Planning a kind presence is one of the most straightforward and most powerful practices you can do to add more joy to your world.

Day 45

People throwing darts at you likely have an unhealthy relationship with the self. Those unkind to others are often unkind to themselves.

A senior colleague of mine, let's call him Peter, who would evaluate my performance, became increasingly judgmental of me for a few years. He wanted me to conform and not do anything innovative. I found it challenging to be in the same room as him, until I met one of his previous supervisors.

His supervisor shared in confidence that the last few years were very trying for Peter. Peter felt he could have done much better but made some disappointing career choices. Perhaps, his personal frustration was coming out as cynicism and negativity. This awareness helped evoke compassion in me. It became much easier to work with Peter from thereon. However, his behavior didn't quite change.

Looking back, I am grateful to Peter because he helped me grow in many ways, both emotionally and in my work.

I think it's fair and helpful to assume that someone throwing a dart at you has an unhealthy relationship with the self. This awareness will empower you not to give any more importance to that person than they deserve.

So, think today of why someone unkind may be having low self-worth. It might help you feel compassion for that person. This compassion doesn't mean you will enable that person. All it means is that you won't let that person tickle your amygdala, take up a large amount of your brain's real estate, or lower your self-worth.

☐

Day 46

Just as a scrubber is to dishes, our adversaries are to us. They might sound annoying, but in the long term, they help us shine.

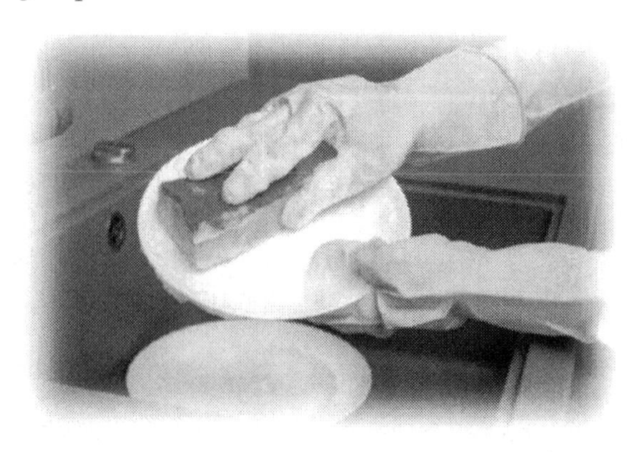

I do have a troll on social media. This person is very skilled at finding the slightest crack in anything I post and is terrific at giving negative feedback. Earlier I used to be annoyed by him, but now I feel grateful.

His comments have helped my work. When not sure, I view my work with his lens. That immediately gives me ideas on how to improve my writing, including the thoughts I am sharing with you.

When I look back, I feel he could get beneath my skin because I let him. I felt like a failure when someone didn't agree with me or pointed at my mistake. That is simply impossible. No matter how careful or good you are, a group of people will rise to oppose you. Once I did an online search on some of the best people in the world. Each one of them had multiple web pages committed to the idea that they were a fraud.

So, you have a choice. Either accept that a proportion of people in the world won't like you. Take their help to remain humble, leverage their feedback to grow, and be grateful for them. Or resent them, get angry, and lower your self-worth.

I would vote for the first option and appreciate my adversaries who challenge me and thus help me grow. Give that a try today and see how you feel.

Day 47

If all the musical instruments sounded identical, there would be no orchestra. Appreciate, honor, value, and welcome our differences.

A soccer team has 11 players. You have a goalkeeper, defenders, midfielders, and forwards, each with their strength. A team that has only defenders won't win, neither will a team with only forwards. Hence the reason to value our differences and unique strengths.

The same applies to different musical instruments in a performance, the flowers in a bouquet, the trees in a forest, the colors on a rainbow, the fruits in a market. If all 88 keys on a piano sounded identical, there would be no music. Variety makes life interesting and meaningful.

We become unkind to each other when we start fighting to create uniformity. That's not only a recipe for building a cruel society but also an unproductive and unsuccessful one.

Today, more than ever, notice and then appreciate, honor, welcome, and value our differences.

Interestingly, the more differences you value, the more similarities you will find, helping you nurture a better relationship with others and the self.

☐

Day 48

The world is a giant tree, and we all are individual leaves on the tree, distinct yet profoundly connected.

Think about this. With the way molecules are recycled in nature, it is possible, actually very likely, that we all have a few molecules that were once in Mother Teresa, Abraham Lincoln, Marie Curie, and anyone else you admire and adore. We all are connected in ways more than we know or can know.

During travels, I used to worry, "What if someone crazy is on the flight with me who will rush to the cockpit." I couldn't relax. Then I started telling myself, "Everyone on the flight is my family. They have similar concerns and dreams as I do." This simple thought transformed my flying experience.

It's a small world friend. It truly is.

You are constantly exchanging molecules with everyone living in your city.

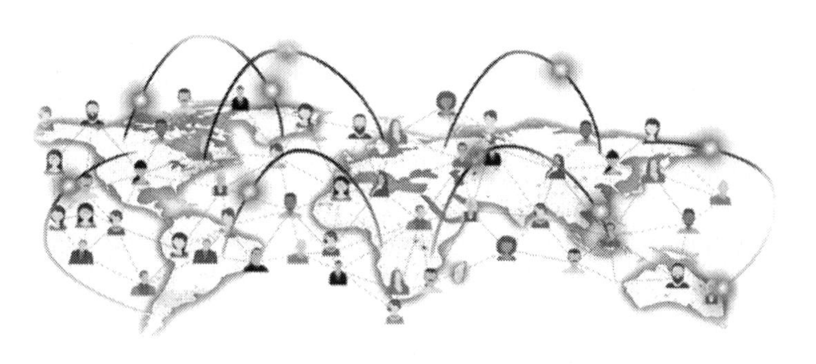

While we all seem separate at the gross level, we all are intimately connected at the subtle level.

So, consider thinking creatively today of a few ways you are connected to others. It will help you grow kindness for loved ones and strangers alike. It will also help you love yourself a little more.

Day 49

Here are the six key ideas we learned this week. Pick the one that makes the most sense to you for today.

- ☐ *On your path to remarkable success, you'll invariably run into unanticipated hurdles. See your step-backs as move forwards. Leverage them to continue to grow.*
- ☐ *In today's world, there is a better than one in two chance that the person in front of you feels vulnerable and lonely. So, smile, say hello, and send a silent good wish to the person in front of you.*
- ☐ *Remember that most people throwing darts at you likely have an unhealthy relationship with the self. When you nurture compassion toward them, you disempower these people from disturbing you or taking too much space in your brain's real estate.*
- ☐ *Just as a scrubber is to dishes, our adversaries are to us. They might sound annoying, but in the long term, they help us shine. Do the best you can to value people who have opposed you in the past.*
- ☐ *If all the musical instruments sounded identical, there would be no orchestra. Appreciate, honor, value, and welcome our differences.*
- ☐ *The world is a giant tree, and we all are individual leaves on the tree, distinct yet profoundly connected. While we all seem separate from each other, at a subtle level, we all are deeply united. Find warmth for others by feeling that connection.*

I pray you find hope and healing today.

Day 50

With the world full of so much pain, seeking happiness just for the self might provoke guilt. The best way to find happiness is to stumble on it while seeking hope and healing for others.

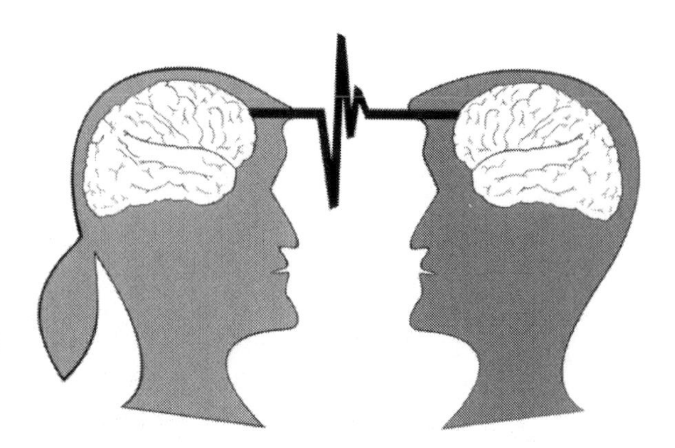

Our brain is designed as a social organ. Research shows when you see another person in pain, physical or emotional, your own pain network fires. Many of us would gladly take our children's pain on our own bodies. Our loved one's pain hurts us more than our personal pain.

I'm sure you'll agree that a large part of the world is stressed right now. Seeing the world in pain gets your pain network active. If you are a kind and sensitive person, you'll struggle with finding lasting happiness when you see the world around you in duress, particularly if you aren't able to do anything about it.

Presently, I feel one of the best ways to be happy is to chance upon joy while seeking hope and healing for others. Research strongly supports this thesis. Volunteering and compassion both engage the brain's reward network.

So, if you want to be happier today, think of ways you can help someone else feel more hopeful.

I wish you a lifetime of happiness.

☐

Day 51

A farmer feeds the nation, a teacher educates the world, a hospital janitor saves lives. Align your work with the deepest purpose—to better negotiate the annoying and the stressful.

A single vote may not move the needle, but each vote is precious and contributes to the country's will. A single neuron doesn't make the brain, but each neuron is precious and contributes to your conscious experience.

Similarly, if you are a farmer, you are an essential part of the network of farmers feeding the nation and the world. The same applies to a teacher, a janitor, a doctor, a professor, a nurse, a social worker, an electrician, and more.

Look at how you contribute to the world with the lens of how every person in your profession collectively helps and serves others. Just as a neuron can't be separated from the brain, you can't be separated from everyone in the world who does what you do.

So, look at your personal meaning in this broader context. Also, keep in mind that we all are collaborating to help build a better world for our planet's children.

Once, I struggled with finding the energy to see the day's final patient. I focused on finding meaning. This patient was a principal of a public school. I thought of hundreds, perhaps thousands of children who might be helped if he stayed positive and resilient. With this thought, I found the energy I needed.

Motivation is a strong source of energy. So, today, think of the deeper purpose of your work. It might give you a little extra pep you can use during the day.

Day 52

Today, if we are privileged to be grateful, then we have a responsibility to be compassionate.

Gratitude puts you in a state of contentment. Gratitude reminds you of your blessings. Happiness thus is a byproduct of feeling grateful.

A lot has to happen for you to feel grateful. You experience something good; you recognize the good, find it special, and then you feel thankful for it. At that moment, you also want nothing real bad overwhelming your mind.

Surprisingly, your genes also influence your gratitude. A particular gene called CD38 that codes for the oxytocin receptor, when it doesn't express itself fully, elevates your gratitude threshold. Your brain then struggles with looking for and finding the positive.

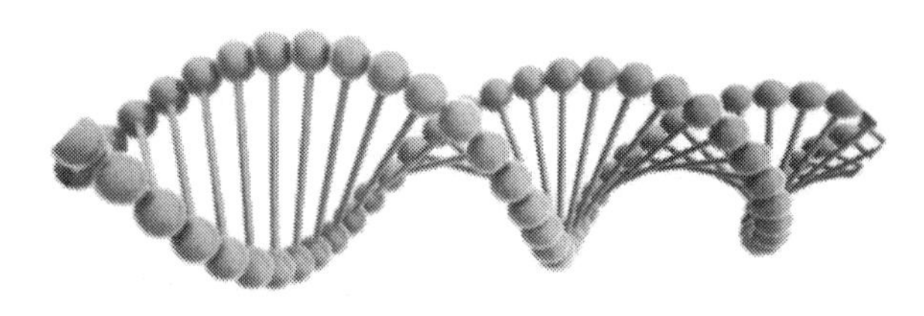

Recognize that many of us struggle to feel grateful either because good things aren't happening in our lives, or we aren't able to appreciate all the goodness because of our brain's limitations, some of which could be genetically programmed.

So, think about someone you know who isn't easy to please. If you are able to feel grateful today, feel compassionate toward this person for his limitation, and for all those who are genetically predisposed to experience high levels of stress and burnout.

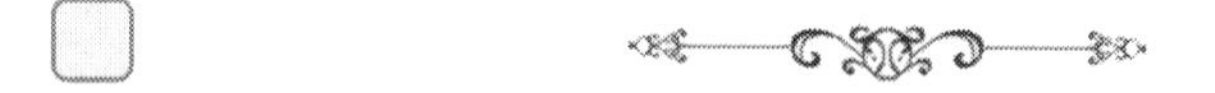

Day 53

Authenticity is more important than positivity. Feeling emotions that are congruent with reality is more helpful than forcing happiness.

An author I once heard shared this personal story. He had five children. He lost one of his children in a freak skiing accident. A well-meaning mourner walked up to him at the church and said, "At least you have the other four. You can feel good about that." Won't you agree that at the time, that was one of the worst things anyone could have said?

We need not find the positive in everything. There is a place for grief, sadness, anger, and fear. In fact, research shows that truly happy people do not force positivity. They allow themselves to experience authentic emotions that are congruent with reality.

Have you been around those high-energy people who are always too optimistic? They are fatiguing to be around. I try to avoid them whenever I can.

Negative emotions help us recognize what's wrong and needs to be fixed. Negative emotions honor our struggles or the person who is struggling whose thoughts make us sad.

I think it's fair to surmise that sometimes, a smile comes only after the heart is emptied of tears.

So, instead of feeling bad today about your negative emotions, or forcing positivity, think and log a few reasons why negative emotions can be helpful. Over the long term, allowing yourself to experience authentic emotions will make you happier and more resilient.

Day 54

Just as in the cold, lifeless space, our earth thrives in its bubble of air (our atmosphere), you may have to create your own bubble of positivity if the world around gets cold or chaotic.

Of late, every single day brings something very concerning that draws my attention. Monday it could be my family's health, Tuesday national politics, Wednesday a workplace disagreement, Thursday a new variant that could evade the vaccine, and so on. Most days, it feels like a forest fire coming my way, and I can barely outrun it.

Also, no matter how rational you think, you will find many people opposing it.

Despite all this, I remain committed to staying strong. I feel just like our planet attracts its atmosphere in the cold, lifeless space, I am called to wrap myself in the quilt of healthy self-worth, hope, courage, love, inspiration, and faith.

Think of the perspectives and resources that make your hope blanket. Is it the memory of prior accomplishments, the energy of your loved ones, the promise of meaning, faith, and more?

Today, take note of all that contributes to your strength. It will lift your day.

Day 55

It is nearly impossible to feel bad about yourself during moments you wish others well. Wish others well to enhance your self-worth.

Your connection with others can be of three types—adversarial, transactional, and affiliative. I try my best to avoid adversarial interactions. Fortunately, they are rare because even one or two such interactions can spoil a week, even a month.

Most interactions are either transactional or affiliative. Transactional interactions are like soup without salt or ice cream without any sweetness. They aren't satisfying. The good news is it takes very little to convert transactional moments into affiliative ones. One simple practice is to wish others well silently.

Once walking in the mall, I decided to send a silent good wish to everyone I saw. I assumed that every person here, even though they seem happy, have struggles and are priceless for someone. That simple practice completely changed my one hour that day.

Since your brain can discern only one conscious experience at any moment, when you choose to send a silent good wish to someone, you can't feel bad about yourself, angry, or frustrated right at that moment. Sending silent good wishes also enhances your self-worth.

So, try and send a silent good wish to at least five people today. Just to challenge yourself, make sure you include at least one person who mildly annoys you in your good wish.

Day 56

Here are the six key ideas we learned this week. Pick the one that makes the most sense to you for today.

- [ ] *Happiness is most easily obtained by sharing it. With the world full of so much pain, seeking happiness just for the self might provoke guilt. The best way to find happiness is to chance upon it while seeking hope and healing for others.*
- [ ] *A farmer feeds the nation, a teacher educates the world, a hospital janitor saves lives. Align your work with your deepest purpose—to better negotiate the annoying and the stressful.*
- [ ] *Gratitude helps but isn't easy to come by for everyone. Today, if you feel grateful for your life's blessings, then choose to feel compassion for those who can't presently access gratitude.*
- [ ] *Authenticity is more important than positivity. Feeling emotions that are congruent with reality is more helpful than forcing happiness.*
- [ ] *Just as in the cold, lifeless space, our earth thrives in its bubble of air (our atmosphere), you may have to create your bubble of positivity if the world around gets cold or chaotic.*
- [ ] *It is nearly impossible to feel bad about yourself during moments you wish others well. Wish others well to enhance your self-worth.*

I pray you find hope and healing today.

WEEKS 9-10

Theme: Live with dignity and grace
Inspiring figure: Rosa Parks

Famously called "the first lady of civil rights," Rosa Parks grew in a segregated world that she resented. Her refusal to give up her seat was the culmination of decades of her learning in defiance and equality. The resulting arrest and her "quiet strength" sparked a drive that made segregation unconstitutional and launched the Civil Rights Movement.

Here are three of Park's most inspiring quotes:

"You must never be fearful about what you are doing when it is right."

"The only tired I was, was tired of giving in."

"No."

Day 57

When you say No, you aren't being unkind. You are being kind to yourself.

Who knows how our world would have been if Rosa Parks had said yes when every part of her wanted to say No. Thankfully, she chose the path of courage. By saying No, she wasn't trying to insult others. She was being respectful to herself.

I hope you are surrounded by kind, understanding people who do not put you in awkward spots where you have to say No very often. I like the idea of a sandwiched No for the occasional No you have to say to preserve your sanity. Sandwiched NO is a No that sits between two Yeses.

For example, if you are invited for dinner that you can't attend, instead of saying I can't come, you could say—Yes, I would love to come, but sorry I am already committed for that day, how about a cup of coffee next Tuesday? This is a No sandwiched between two Yeses.

A specific type of No is you stopping doing something that isn't a good use of your time. For example, you can cut down your dose of headline news, quit folding laundry to perfection, tolerate a few extra weeds in the yard, be okay with a few dirty dishes in the sink—to preserve your time and, in some instances, your sanity.

So, practice saying sandwiched No when you have to say No and add one item today to your Not-To-Do list—something you choose not to do because it doesn't enrich your life.

Day 58

Research shows courageous people don't have less fear. They choose to keep going despite the fear.

Amygdala is the part of the brain that hosts fear. Neuroscience literature talks about a patient named SM who damaged both her amygdala. As a result, she lost fear. She would play with snakes and spiders, including tarantulas as if they were toys. She couldn't assess people's trustworthiness and would repeatedly put herself in harm's way. She has been held at knife points and gun points several times and nearly died in a domestic assault. So, we need our amygdala to be safe. Nature has preserved fear for purpose.

But nature has also given us brain areas that host courage. Your courage tames fear; fear makes sure courage doesn't become careless. Research shows you have brain areas that host courage. The more active these areas, the more courageous you feel. You can also intentionally activate these courage areas.

Finding meaning is an important path to activating your brain's courage network. The more profound the meaning you are serving, the better your ability to overcome your fear.

Every species has to keep going despite the fear; butterflies, penguins, birds, lions, buffaloes, elephants, zebras, every species. Buffaloes are ready to stand up to lions when they are protecting their calf. The meaning helps them overcome their fear.

No doubt, friend, the force of meaning is stronger than the friction of fear. Right here, at this moment, you can leverage the force of meaning by thinking about it.

Ask yourself in the next few moments, what are some compelling reasons for you to keep going? Your answers will fill you with the courage to better negotiate life's narrow lanes.

Day 59

Go back to your earliest memories and spend a few minutes thinking about the people who helped you feel worthy and loved.

Every time I go back to my earliest memories and think about a teacher who helped me through difficult moments, I think of Mr. Kami. Mr. Kami knew just the right words to say when I didn't perform well, which was quite often. He believed in me when I didn't believe in myself. And he wasn't shy of showing his approval. I am so grateful to him.

We all come across such people at least a few times in our life. If we are lucky, we get to spend enough time with them so their warmth and wisdom can touch and transform us. Very likely, one or more such people helped your career and your life.

Thinking about these people helps you visit happier areas of your brain.

Today, take a few minutes and think about one or more people who helped you the most in your life's struggles. Can you recall a few words they had said about you?

Just thinking about them and writing their name might help you feel stronger and more hopeful, lifting your moment.

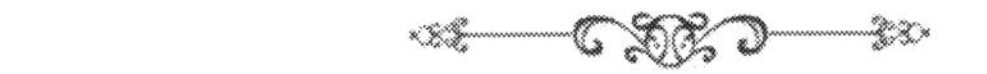

Day 60

Worries deplete your today without nourishing your tomorrow. You can't rid yourself of all the worries, but you can choose to dilute them with hope, courage, and faith.

Our brains have a phenomenal ability to imagine and think. Right now, you can take your attention to an orchard and see the oranges, the moon and watch all the craters, in a mall and look at all the different showrooms, into a dream you saw last night, or the farthest reaches of the universe.

Interestingly, if a researcher were to track your brain's activity, it would look similar when you are actually watching or just imagining the moon's craters. That's why our worries are so powerful. With worries, you experience what you are worried about as if it happened. Worries thus deplete your today. Worries also usurp the time you would otherwise have used to overcome adversity or savor the present moment.

When worrying, you are experiencing the future load and bypassing this moment.

Now, we can't eliminate worries because we can't eliminate our brain's ability to imagine. We can, however, dilute the worries—with hope, courage, and faith.

A simple way to rethink your worries is to think about how you have overcome your previous struggles. That simple memory will remind you that you are stronger than you think.

So, take a note today of some of the most courageous things you have done, what gives you hope, and perhaps your thoughts about spirituality. It will help dilute your worries.

Day 61

Our barrier to compassion isn't the absence of it; it is limiting our compassion to a select few who we believe deserve our compassion.

In an interesting study, a few new immigrants were shown the locals having a painful procedure. The immigrants had minimal change in their brain's activity. The same study was repeated with immigrants who had been in the country for over five years. Their pain areas now lit up when they saw the locals going through a painful procedure. You can see how we start sharing and experiencing the pain of those with whom we relate.

We all have brain areas that host compassion. The barrier to compassion is limiting activation of our compassion network for a select few people who we feel deserve our compassion, particularly the people we find similar to us or connected to us.

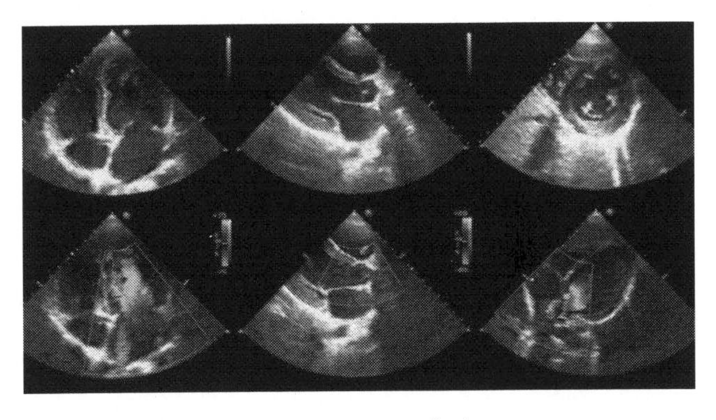

Several years ago, I spent a lot of time looking at echocardiograms of the heart. I couldn't tell from looking at the inside whose heart it was. We are more similar to each other and also more connected than we know or can ever know. Knowing this might expand your zone of compassion today just a little bit.

So, think of expanding your compassion to a few people or groups who you may have judged in the past. It will help you become a happier and better human being.

Day 62

Excessive fear makes us irrational, and irrationality increases fear. Let your fears keep you safe and not paralyze you into inaction.

When you are in fear because of a real or imaginary threat, you release lots of adrenaline in your system. This adrenaline effectively paralyzes the rational areas of your brain. It is these brain areas that help you integrate multiple perspectives to come to a rational conclusion. Fear thus leads to irrationality.

Irrationality takes away the mentorship of your brain's higher centers, particularly the pre-frontal cortex on your amygdala. With the amygdala on its own, fear starts dominating the thinking. You can thus see how fear causes irrationality and irrationality breeds fear—locking you in a downward spiral.

Individuals, societies, and countries do cruel things when imaginary fears make them irrational. I am sure you have witnessed some of that in your lifetime. I hope you and I do not ever have to see that in the future. I strongly feel that understanding this science can help everyone, including those in charge of important decisions.

For today, think of some unhelpful irrational fears that you're willing to shed, even if for the next few hours, to feel lighter and be more productive.

☐

Day 63

Here are the six key ideas we learned this week. Pick the one that makes the most sense to you for today.

- [ ] *Remember that when you say No, you aren't being unkind. You are being kind to yourself.*

- [ ] *Research shows courageous people don't have less fear. They choose to keep going despite the fear. One of the best ways to increase your courage is by finding meaning.*

- [ ] *Go back to your earliest memories and spend a few minutes thinking about the people who helped you feel worthy and loved. Thinking about these people will help you feel grateful and strong.*

- [ ] *Worries deplete your today without nourishing your tomorrow. You can't rid yourself of all the concerns, but you can choose to dilute them with hope, courage, and faith.*

- [ ] *Our barrier to compassion isn't the absence of it; it is limiting our compassion to a select few who we believe deserve our compassion. Consider expanding your zone of compassion to one person you may have judged in the past.*

- [ ] *Excessive fear makes us irrational, and irrationality increases fear. Let your fears keep you safe and not paralyze you into inaction. Let go of one or more irrational fears today.*

I pray you find hope and healing today.

Day 64

We all are profoundly similar to each other, much more than we are different. Finding similarities helps us become kinder.

As a first-year medical student, I learned of normal ranges. In health, we maintain a narrow range of blood levels of sodium, potassium, pH, chloride, calcium, phosphorus, and so many other compounds.

Later in my training, I heard the heartbeats, lung sounds, intestinal gurgles—the sounds we all produce and that are very similar amongst us.

The way our eyes focus, our kidneys cleanse the blood, the liver metabolizes, the joints move, the skin heals—is all so similar.

The advantage of thinking about these similarities is that research shows the more we focus on what unites us, the more compassionate we become. The secret to compassion is finding commonalities—biological, psychological, social, and spiritual.

Today, think of a few similarities between you and someone you find annoying. Perhaps that person has

similar dreams and concerns as you, has similar constraints, shared hurts and losses, and more. You and that person might even have a common ancestor.

Finding similarities will deepen your compassion and start your process of healing.

☐

Day 65

Sometimes, it helps to notice a neighborhood yard with more weeds, to enjoy yours with fewer.

A few years ago, I called to talk to my cousin. He sounded sad and stressed.

"What happened," I asked.

"I had my yearly evaluation. I got a 5% raise and was promoted one level."

"So, what's the problem?"

"Well, one of my colleagues got a 10% raise and received a double promotion."

My cousin was stuck in an upward social comparison. He compared himself with someone who had it much better. At least in his eyes. He didn't notice the hard work his colleague had put in. He also didn't see that many of his other colleagues didn't get any raises or promotions. I spent some time helping him zoom out. It seemed to help, at least at that moment.

Upward social comparison can help you by inspiring you to work harder and smarter. But such a comparison, if it makes you envious and miserable, doesn't help.

Feel inspired by someone more successful and notice what you can learn from that person about how you can do better.

At the same time, feel grateful in the awareness that most of what you have is perhaps someone else's dream.

So, think today of a few ways you have been uniquely blessed. It might help you feel energized.

Day 66

Trees can teach you selflessness, dogs-love, toddlers-curiosity, weeds-hardiness, dolphins-play. Pick your teacher for today.

Every species alive and extinct can teach us something. Trees hold the soil together, produce life-giving oxygen, cool the planet, provide fruits, wood, shade, and more. In life and death, they serve the world.

Dogs return the food, shelter, and love they receive with unconditional devotion, boundless love, and joy to their owners. I know of many instances where dogs have helped a person recover from physical or emotional crisis and even saved their owner's life.

Toddlers are a bundle of curiosity. They are particularly curious about faces, colors, and anything new and different. It is this curiosity instinct that helps them learn so much in such a short time.

Weeds are hardy, need little to grow, flower, and multiply. Weeds seem like they have a can-do attitude and keep pushing undeterred, despite our efforts to eliminate them. At least that's what I feel about the weeds in my yard.

Dolphins convert their daily chores—swimming, hunting, or just hanging out—into play. They seem like always having fun. Dolphins teach us that it takes just a small effort to change the flavor of your experience and convert it into something enjoyable to watch and experience.

Today, think of the life lessons you can learn from trees, dogs, toddlers, weeds, and dolphins. Perhaps one of them might inspire you to feel better and stronger.

Day 67

"What's the ultimate meaning of life?" is a difficult question. A better question is: How can I make my life more meaningful?

The world is immense and unknowable. If the life of the Universe was one year, then modern human history started just in the last few seconds. If the entire solar system was as big as a grain of sand, then the Universe would still stretch tens of millions of miles.

Even back home on our planet, we have explored only about 5% of the oceans that make 70% of the earth's surface.

While we know a lot, it is still very little. It is like knowing the first word in a 100 volume Encyclopedia. How can then we be confident about the entire knowledge in all the volumes?

The ultimate meaning of life is thus tough to answer. Perhaps a better question than the ultimate meaning of life is to ask how I can make my life a little more meaningful?

Answering the first question with a firm conviction could be a reflection of our ignorance. Interestingly, answering the second question may take us closer to the correct answer of the first.

So, think of what matters to you the most. How can you make your life a little more meaningful?

Guided by that thought, find one way you can add more meaning to your days. That will make your days and your life worthwhile.

☐ 

Day 68

The dominating and the dominated both live in fear. Joy and fulfillment are in feeling equal and helping others feel equal.

In nature, one of the best relationships is that of symbiosis—where two members support each other in some important essential way. When we try to dominate a system, we end up destabilizing it. And if we depend on the very system we are trying to dominate, the instability we create ends up hurting us. We have done that to planet earth, fellow human beings, animals, plants, and more.

A much better relationship is that of collaboration, partnership, or friendship. It is best to assume that we all are equal, contributing equally in a positive, meaningful way in each of these relationships. No one needs to dominate.

One perspective that might help us nurture the idea of equality is learning the dollar value of the human body. The 11 elements in our body—oxygen, carbon, hydrogen, nitrogen, calcium, phosphorus, potassium, sodium, chlorine, magnesium, and sulfur—are worth only a few dollars—no matter whose body is their source.

At the other extreme, the spark of life within us, our spiritual essence, is worth trillions—within each one of us. So, however you wish to see our individual value—we are trivial or priceless, or even both—consider everyone equal.

Think in your own way about how you can nurture the idea of equality. Such thinking will help you feel less vulnerable and more connected.

Day 69

Many stuff toys look prettier and much more flawless than the original. If it were just about beauty and perfection, we would be living with stuff-toy partners.

Interesting research shows when people try to lose weight, if they set an unreasonably high expectation—such as losing 50 pounds in a month—they not only fail at achieving that goal, but they also quit their effort altogether. For many endeavors in life, practical and achievable is more valuable than perfect and unrealistic.

Similarly, if you expect perfection from others, they will fail you. A person who is phenomenal at organizing the closet might be exacting about many other aspects of life, to the point of annoying you, if you are an easy-going, happy-go-lucky person. Best not to expect a person to be totally organized about one aspect and completely flexible about others. It helps to remember that we are all a package deal.

Further, the more you get to know someone, the more imperfections you will find. Look at the moon with a pair of binoculars, and you will see all the craters. It is best to adjust for this binocular effect.

A perfect world with perfect people could exist in stories but isn't real. Such a world will actually be more miserable than you can imagine. I will leave that discussion for another date.

For now, ponder over some of the most profound timeless qualities in your partner or friend and disregard their few imperfections. It will help you be kind to them and yourself, both wonderful for your relationship.

Day 70

Here are the six key ideas we learned this week. Pick the one that makes the most sense to you for today.

- [ ] *We all are profoundly similar to each other, much more than we are different. The more similarities you find with others, the kinder you will become.*
- [ ] *Sometimes, it helps to notice a neighborhood yard with more weeds, to enjoy yours with fewer. This is particularly true for days when you feel frustrated or disappointed.*
- [ ] *Trees can teach you selflessness, dogs-love, toddlers-curiosity, weeds-hardiness, dolphins-play. Pick your teacher for today.*
- [ ] *"What's the ultimate meaning of life?" is a difficult question. A better question is: How can I make my life a little more meaningful? Think of one thing you can do today to add more meaning to your days.*
- [ ] *The dominating and the dominated both live in fear. Joy and fulfillment are in feeling equal and helping others feel equal. Think of perspectives that will help you feel equal to others.*
- [ ] *Many stuff toys look prettier and more perfect than the original. If it were just about beauty and perfection, we would be living with stuff-toy partners. Today, focus more on the qualities in the people closest to you that are timeless and not just the superficial appearances.*

I pray you find hope and healing today.

WEEKS 11-12

Theme: Be humble, be curious
Inspiring figure: Alexander Fleming

Not many can claim that their work has saved over a hundred million lives. One of them was the humble Alexander Fleming. His curiosity and brilliance found a hidden antibiotic (Penicillin) in a petri dish that was accidentally left open and grew mold that inhibited the surrounding bacteria. Penicillin has influenced advances in almost every medical field, including surgery and organ transplants.

Here are three of Fleming's most inspiring quotes:

"The unprepared mind cannot see the outstretched hand of opportunity."

"My only merit is that I did not neglect the observation."

"Nature makes penicillin; I just found it."

Day 71

It helps to consider an unplanned detour an adventure. Such an outlook saves you energy to find your way back to the highway.

Several events and attributes came together to help the discovery of penicillin. Alexander Fleming's habit of keeping his lab dirty seeded the mold. His two-week vacation allowed enough time for the mold to grow and secrete the antibiotic that inhibited the bacterial growth on the culture plate.

It was Fleming's curiosity and astute observation that converted the unplanned and annoying growth of the mold into a transforming insight—that the mold was secreting something that could be of value to humanity. A deeper look and creative collaborations led to the isolation and eventual mass production of the antibiotic, saving hundreds of millions of lives and making many other medical innovations possible.

Consider modest failures, missteps, losses, mistakes—as adventures that might help you in ways you may not presently understand. This attitude will help you learn and grow because of these experiences, converting them into success, sometimes transformative changes.

Think today of an instance when an annoying delay or a mistake in the past turned out to be eventually helpful to you. It might give you a helpful perspective to better handle the present and future delays and mistakes.

Day 72

In the sky today, you can see the same dull clouds or a formation never seen before. Every boring day offers you the same choice.

In a study, researchers gave participants a choice to either sit alone and get bored or give themselves painful electric shocks during that time. You will be surprised, or perhaps not surprised, that the majority chose to give themselves painful electric shocks. Our brain finds the emotional pain of boredom more painful than the pain of a modest physical injury.

The challenge is that, unlike hunter-gatherers, we live in the same home with the same kitchen and bedroom, go to the same workplace, and drive the same automobile. The physical world thus doesn't offer enough novelty.

So, what's the solution? Manufacture your novelty to keep life interesting.

When you have a few spare minutes, try simple novelty exercises like, compare the design of your hands with that of your loved ones or friends, find unique shapes in cloud formations, carefully study the front cover of your favorite book to observe details you had missed previously, try to memorize the logo of your favorite brand, and perhaps redraw that logo, and more.

Think of how the simplest of experiences can be really interesting. Try to make it interesting by noticing a minor detail and make a connection you hadn't thought of before. Such an attitude will convert a dull day into one full of fun, meaning, and learning.

☐ 

Day 73

Success is preceded and followed by failure. If you're successful, rest assured you'll fail; if you're failing, rest assured you'll succeed.

During childhood, I fantasized about living at a place where it was a perpetual day so that I could play all the time. Well, Svalbard, Norway is one such place where the sun doesn't set from mid-April to mid-August. Closer to home for you and me, there isn't a perpetual day or night. Sunrise is followed by sunset, which is followed by sunrise. That's the norm of the world.

Similarly, success and failure are in lockstep with each other. Success is followed by failure, and failure is followed by success. In every success something could have gone better but didn't; in every failure something could have gone worse but didn't.

In success, the knowledge that some day you'll fail, will help you stay humble through the celebration. In failure, the knowledge that one day you'll again succeed will help you stay hopeful and inspired through the gloom.

Today, think of how a previous failure may have seeded your today's success or a present failure might seed a future success. It will help you embrace failure with a more open heart.

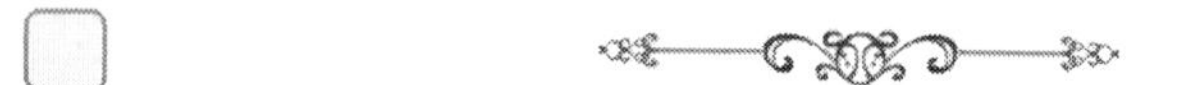

Day 74

Humility isn't low self-worth. Humility knows that you are worthy, just as others are. Humility accepts praise where due and is generous in praising others.

Neil Armstrong, the first person to walk on the moon, remained human and humble till the very end. Responding to his fame, he said, "No, I just don't deserve it. Circumstance put me into that particular role. That wasn't planned by anyone." My understanding is that one reason he was chosen to be the first human to land on the moon was his humility. In the words of his flight director Christ Kraft, "He had no ego."

Humility brings you more gifts than you can imagine. Humility helps you be kind. As a humble person, you are less likely to be annoyed. You are more helpful to others and a better learner. People like to hang out around you because they feel worthy and validated in your presence.

Today, spend a few seconds thinking about a few humble people in your life. Think of a few reasons you like these people.

It might inspire you to embrace a bit extra humility today.

Day 75

Your patience is your treat to others and yourself. When you gift them your patience, you gift yourself peace and happiness.

Think of ordering pizza on a stormy day with a bad phone connection. You are ordering a large thin crust pizza, half cheese, half veggie with toppings of mushrooms, onions, and bell pepper. You want extra cheese on the cheesy side. How will the transaction go if you and the pizza person are wanting on patience? You know the answer.

Your patience is your gift to others, and their patience is their gift to you. Patience not only feels good, but your patience also improves your physical health, work performance, financial success, relationships, and decreases the risk of heart attack, accidents, and premature death. The only thing impatience accelerates is aging.

Developing patience, however, isn't easy as flipping on a switch. Expecting us to become fully patient all day long is a tall expectation. Instead, it might help to sprinkle moments of intentional patience multiple times during the day.

Think of at least one time during the day when you are likely to be impatient. Choose to be extra patient during that time today. It will start your journey into patience and calm.

Day 76

Notice for a few seconds the color of your loved one's eyes. This little practice can boost your oxytocin (the bonding hormone) and fill you with joy.

Several research studies show that when mothers and babies gaze at each other's eyes, they release oxytocin in their body. The same happens with dogs. The more owners gaze at their dog's eyes and dogs at owner's, the greater the release of oxytocin in both of them. Researchers believe that this mutual oxytocin release created the blue tooth connection between the two species.

I believe there is something special about our eyes. The eyes are an offshoot of the brain, likely the most intricate part of our body. The eyes are also considered the most attractive and expressive part of our face. Researchers have found that our ability to read others' emotions most significantly depends on the expressions in our eyes.

But when I ask people to think about the last time they paused to look at the color of their loved ones' eyes, the response often is, "Like eighteen years ago!"

That's such a lost opportunity, I feel.

Go to your Smartphone's photo stream and zoom in at the eyes of some of your loved ones and friends. When you meet someone dear today, pause for 2 seconds to look at the color of their eyes. Now pause for only two seconds and not two minutes, otherwise, you'll freak them out!

Noticing their eyes will help you pull positivity out of thin air.

Day 77

Here are the six key ideas we learned this week. Pick the one that makes the most sense to you for today.

- ☐ *It helps to consider an unplanned detour an adventure. Such an outlook saves you energy to find your way back to the highway.*
- ☐ *In the sky today, you can see the same dull clouds or a formation never seen before. Every boring day offers you the same choice. Choose wisely.*
- ☐ *Success is preceded and followed by failure. If you're successful, stay humble, knowing that you'll fail; if you're failing, stay inspired, knowing that you'll succeed.*
- ☐ *Humility isn't low self-worth. Humility knows that you are worthy, just as others are. Humility accepts praise where due and is generous in praising others.*
- ☐ *Your patience is your treat to others and yourself. When you gift them your patience, you gift yourself peace and happiness. Consider being a little extra patient today.*
- ☐ *Notice for a few seconds the color of your loved one's eyes. This little practice can boost your oxytocin (the bonding hormone) and fill you with joy.*

I pray you find hope and healing today.

Day 78

Something novel draws attention. Interestingly, when we start paying attention, what seemed ordinary starts looking novel.

A toddler can spend hours discovering new details in a simple toy. But when we grow up, we lose that sense of curiosity and get bored within a few minutes.

Here is a small suggestion for today. Pick a familiar object—an apple, a key, a book, or something else. Now, choose to look at this object for two minutes with the goal of finding at least three extra details you hadn't noticed before.

If you can't find an object, examine your own hand, noticing the map of different lines carved on your palm.

Continue further reading only after you have noticed three new details of an object or the roadmap on your hand.

Perhaps, with this little practice, you discovered extra novelty in your world.

That's the bidirectional relationship between novelty and attention. A novel object draws attention, and when you choose to pay attention, you start finding greater novelty.

So, here is a starter kit of five items for improving your attention:

Memorize your car's license plate number and try to notice one detail on your license plate you hadn't observed before.

Open your photo stream and notice the color of the eyes of at least three of your family members or friends.

Between the pointer and the ring finger, do you know which finger is longer in your hand?

Carefully study the design of the front cover of your favorite book. Draw this design on a blank paper.

Write your name and draw a ladybug with your non-dominant hand.

I hope this little practice will help your attention, increase your familiarity with your world, and you'll also have some fun doing it.

Day 79

I was much wiser in kindergarten. I knew sharing. I knew how to laugh, hug, and love. I could forget myself for hours.

Allow me to introduce you to a very wise person. This person is conscientious, loving, kind, well-meaning, pure, curious, and has only a tiny ego.

Perhaps you guessed who I am talking about. This special person is a kindergartener. And this attribute applies to all kindergarteners—millions of them.

I believe deep within us is a seed of wisdom and morality. This seed starts in innocence. But often, this treasure gets buried behind our biases, desires, and unhealthy learnings.

A good life is when you nourish your innocence with knowledge, experience, and compassion, and convert it into wisdom. I so wish this transformation defined every person's life.

It can if you choose to take charge and will this transformation.

If you wish to kindle that process today, think of a child in your life you adore. Then notice some of the most admirable qualities of this child. Choose to embody at least one of those qualities today. You are on your way to a transformation that will eventually bring you back home.

☐ 

Day 80

Who can be more selfless than a tree that produces seedless fruits? Act like a tree today, sharing your gifts with no expectations of a reward.

In a study involving university students, researchers randomly checked with students multiple times during the day about their present-moment thoughts. More than 50 percent of the time, students were dealing with a self-focused unfulfilled desire. Struggling with such a desire often made them unhappy.

Unlike us, a tree's life is very different. Every part of a tree is useful for the world—the leaves breathe out oxygen, the stem and branches provide wood, the roots keep the soil together, and the fruits nourish us all. Traveling with us on our planet are trillions of silent tree sages living a selfless life.

One could argue that the roots, the stem, the leaves, the flowers, the fruits—they all collaborate to help the tree produce seeds that carry the hope of a future tree. But what about the trees that have seedless fruits? Their fruits serve no purpose for them—other than serving the planet.

So, let's be inspired by the trees today, particularly the ones that produce seedless fruits, and think of ways we can live a more selfless day—living not for a self-focused goal but a world-centric purpose.

And yes, nothing wrong with hugging a tree in your backyard!

☐ 

Day 81

Appreciate what seems easy. It is easy today because someone spent years simplifying what was then difficult or near impossible.

Perhaps you don't think much about life's routine easy activities such as talking, writing, walking, driving. But it took years for you to learn and perfect them. They seem easy because you did a lot of hard work to convert what was difficult and complex into easy.

We wash our dishes in dishwashers, keep our milk refrigerated for weeks, cruise in cars that effortlessly drive faster than a cheetah, and do not have to burn coal in our homes to cook food. All of this wasn't easy in the past and was not available just a few decades ago.

These inventions that have brought so much comfort started as an idea, an initial clumsy product that was then refined over decades, and in some instances, centuries.

Think of some of your daily conveniences that weren't available to your grandparents a hundred years ago. Perhaps, it might help you feel a little extra grateful.

If you want to take the next step, think of converting something difficult or complex into simple and easy for the next generation. That could be a worthwhile project which might keep you busy for a long time.

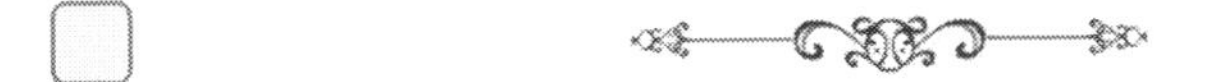

Day 82

See a dad or mom in a cab driver, a son or daughter in the mail person. Look at others from within their circle of love.

I was once standing in line at the bank. I was in a hurry, and the teller seemed particularly slow. I began to lose patience, sensed a surge of adrenaline in my system. This wasn't a comforting feeling. So, I brought my attention to the flow of my breath and began slow deep breathing. That helped, but only a little bit. Then I remembered compassion.

I created a story in my head. I tried to see the teller within her circle of love—as a mom, wife, daughter, sister, niece, friend, colleague, neighbor. "I am sure she has her share of struggles," I thought. What if her child was sick last night? What if she has a back pain today? What if she is worried about misplacing an envelope with a thousand dollars? While none of this may have been true, thinking these thoughts helped me be kind. They took away my impatience.

Kind thoughts are accessible to all of us. If you want to live in a world that loves your children as much as you do, default to kindness. You can start by thinking about why the people around you are more precious than most of us generally believe.

Consider treating everyone today as if they are worth trillions. With this mindset, not only will you and others enjoy your mutual presence, but you will also have a more productive day.

Day 83

We can't inhale without exhaling or exhale without inhaling. We can't give without receiving or receive without giving. It's a circle.

A few months ago, I was assembling a complicated piece of furniture. My nine-year-old daughter hovered around, watching my every move. I enjoyed her admiring attention.

Then she asked how she could help. I hesitated. I didn't want her to get hurt.

That made her sad. Only when I asked her to hold the tools and tighten a few screws was she happy. Helping me made her feel like a big girl. The same applies to all of us.

Helping others, being of value, and contributing to an important purpose enhances our self-worth. Every exchange in life entails receiving and giving, very much like the exchange of the bee and the flower. They both receive and give to each other.

So, those who you get to help are helping you by receiving your help.

Think today of the many ways you can be grateful for the opportunities you have received to serve the world. Such thinking will keep you humble, happy, and useful.

☐

Day 84

Here are the six key ideas we learned this week. Pick the one that makes the most sense to you for today.

- ☐ *Something novel draws attention. Interestingly, when we start paying attention, what seemed ordinary starts looking novel. Find extra details in a daily object to perceive it as novel.*

- ☐ *I was much wiser in kindergarten. I knew sharing. I knew how to laugh, hug, love. I could forget myself for hours. Embody a good attribute of a child in your life.*

- ☐ *Who can be more selfless than a tree that produces seedless fruits? Act like a tree today, sharing your gifts with no expectations of a reward.*

- ☐ *Appreciate what seems easy. It is easy today because someone spent years simplifying what was then difficult or near impossible.*

- ☐ *See a dad or mom in a cab driver, a son or daughter in the mail person. Look at others from within their circle of love.*

- ☐ *We can't inhale without exhaling or exhale without inhaling. We can't give without receiving or receive without giving. It's a circle. Appreciate not only those who help you but also those willing to accept your help.*

I pray you find hope and healing today.

WEEKS 13-14

Theme: Serve the underprivileged
Inspiring figure: Mother Teresa

"Never eat a single mouthful unless you are sharing it with others." That's what Agnes learned from her mother. She became Mother Teresa, having taken the vow of poverty, chastity, and obedience. A Nobel laureate, her Order of the Missionaries of Charity, orphanages, foundations, and hospices serve millions of poor and needy. She was canonized a Saint in 2016.

Here are three of Saint Teresa's most inspiring quotes:

"If you judge people, you have no time to love them."

"Not all of us can do great things. But we can do small things with great love."

"If we have no peace, it is because we have forgotten that we belong to each other."

Day 85

When brewing happiness and love for others, you can't help but first taste it yourself.

Mother Teresa served the poorest of the poor. A reporter once asked Mother Teresa how she remained positive and energized when surrounded by so much misery and disease.

She asked him if he had ever fed a hungry person with his own hands. The reporter said No.

"What good will it do to me?" he asked.

"Come tomorrow, and you'll experience it first-hand," Mother Teresa said.

These words are, of course, paraphrased a bit.

The next day Mother Teresa arranged for the reporter to feed a hungry person with his own hands. The reporter started crying at the end of it—with tears of joy.

A powerful source of happiness and healing is helping and serving others. It is this joy of service that Mother Teresa experienced every day, despite all the struggles.

Comforting others fills us with positive meaning and self-worth—that provides deep nourishment to our soul.

Today, think of a few ways you can help others feel worthy and loved, and give at least one of these ideas a good try. In helping others feel worthy and loved, you'll start feeling worthy and loved.

Day 86

Assume you are a role model for thousands of children. Live your day modeling the right behavior for these children.

This sounds like a familiar story. An inspiring leader or a celebrity shares passionate words of compassion. After the speech is over, not realizing that the mic is still on, he goes back to demeaning and insulting words for the same people he was praising earlier. I am sure you have seen or heard about such incidents.

Many people wear two personas—one private, another public. They behave differently when they are being observed. Email rage is much less common than the abuse we unload using an unrecognizable screen name. Just look at the comments people write in the thread of a news story about a tragic event. You'll be surprised.

An excellent way to remain kind is to assume that someone who matters a lot to you, perhaps a child in your life, is noticing and being affected by your thoughts, words, and actions. That child will model your behavior in her own life.

So, just for today, assume that thousands of children are looking up to you as their role model. Assume that many of them are watching you learn the proper habits and behaviors. With this assumption, you'll live a more fulfilling day, one guided by your deepest values.

Day 87

Replace the word work in your dictionary with service, purpose, and prayer.

I was once visiting the Taj Mahal and surrounding tourist spots. We hired a tour guide to take us around. Let's call him Raj. Raj was a phenomenally energetic and professional person. He shared the intricate details of the place with great passion. He also had excellent command over the local dialect as well as English.

I was fascinated by his skills. I asked Raj how many times he had shown tourists around.

"Like 10,000," he said.

"Don't you get bored," I asked. "How do you maintain such good energy?"

"Because it's not about me," he said with a smile. "It's about the experience I can give to my clients."

I am grateful to Raj for teaching me that even the most repetitive tasks can become engaging when you connect them with a deeper purpose, particularly someone tangibly being helped.

So, think today of how your work brings hope, help, and healing to at least one person. Once you're able to think of that someone, even the most tedious part of your work will feel a little less boring.

Day 88

If you feel lost on the dirt roads today, remember that all small roads eventually meet a highway.

I often disagree when I hear someone say, "I am in the middle of nowhere." Where you are is the center of the universe—the center of your universe.

The neglected corner of the world where Mother Teresa worked became the world's center when her compassion and hard work became known to everyone.

The lab of Alexander Fleming, the prison of Nelson Mandela, the press conferences held by Eleanor Roosevelt—all became the center of the world because of their persona and purpose.

The infinite space in the universe has unlimited centers—each connected to the other, just as all roads eventually connect to a highway.

If you feel bypassed or otherwise lonely, do not feel you are in a neglected corner of the world.

You aren't alone because you are connected to everyone. Where you are is the center of the universe.

☐

Day 89

Compassion isn't just diluting sorrow; it is also multiplying joy. When you are truly, deeply happy for others in their happy moments, you are being compassionate.

Imagine winning a large sum of money in a jackpot. How many people can you call knowing they will be truly happy for you but not want a dime? They are your true friends.

The response to your winning lottery can be –

So happy for you! Let's celebrate.

Or, I'm glad you won the money, but you didn't work hard for it. I slog every day to earn my keep.

The third response can be—Did you know that winning a big lottery increases your risk of early death?

While none of the three responses may be factually wrong, the latter two aren't kind.

Sharing others' sorrows brings you closer to them. Research shows that multiplying joy is even more powerful. You come even closer to the people who open-heartedly are happy in your happiness.

Compassion thus isn't just decreasing others' pain. It is also celebrating together. In fact, celebrating others' success may be more difficult than sharing sorrow.

So, try and find creative ways of participating in others' happy moments. I like the quote that says, "Good friends make the good times better and the hard times easier." Let's put this into practice today.

☐

Day 90

Just as you decorate your face with the right makeup, decorate your mind with gratitude and kindness before starting your day.

Most people I know do something to keep their facial skin healthy and attractive, and rightfully so. Some limit it to foundation and concealer; others do the complete treatment—foundation, concealer, highlighter, eyeliner, mascara, lip liner, lip color, and more. If we don't tend to our face, our skin gets flaky within a day or two, and we start looking unkempt and older. The same applies to the mind.

The mind needs daily decoration with its own makeup. The two essential ingredients of our mind's makeup are gratitude and kindness.

Start with the foundation of kindness. To that, add the concealer of gratitude. Keep in mind that just as you make a little effort every day to look good with the facial makeup, make a little effort every day to feel good with the mental makeup. That effort is truly worth your time.

Here is an excellent first step. Ask yourself: What kind and grateful thoughts can I think at this moment. Intentionally think such positive thoughts, and you are well on your way to building a beautiful mind.

☐

Day 91

Here are the six key ideas we learned this week. Pick the one that makes the most sense to you for today.

- ☐ *When brewing happiness and love for others, you can't help but first taste it yourself. Be the reason someone smiles today.*
- ☐ *Assume you are a role model for thousands of children. Live your day modeling the correct behavior for these children, assuming they are looking up to you every day.*
- ☐ *Replace the word work in your dictionary with service, purpose, and prayer. Connect your work with a higher meaning to find joy in it.*
- ☐ *If you feel lost on the dirt roads today, remember that all small roads eventually meet a highway. Do not feel lonely. Where you are is the center of the universe.*
- ☐ *Compassion isn't just diluting sorrow; it is also multiplying joy. When you are truly, deeply happy for others in their happy moments, you are being compassionate. Show your compassion by being happy in others' happiness.*
- ☐ *Just as you decorate your face with the right makeup, decorate your mind with gratitude and kindness before starting your day.*

I pray you find hope and healing today.

Day 92

Not every pain can be explained by an abnormal MRI scan. Help those struggling feel validated and cared for, not judged and belittled.

Our skin has pain receptors. Our spinal cord has a distinct pathway for nerve cells that carry the pain information. Our brain has assigned areas that interpret the intensity and the relevance of pain. This elaborate machinery informs us about the source of our pain and what we can do about it. Pain keeps us safe.

Yet, we don't like to feel any pain. Pain seems like that friend who we need but would rather avoid.

Every person who is hurting has a reason for the pain. In some, an obvious injury fires the pain receptors. While in others, the pain network activates without any previous injury or at least a known hurt. Scientists don't fully understand why some of us hurt so much despite completely normal scans and other tests. But that doesn't mean their pain is any less. It is real and hurts.

It is these people, in whom all the tests come back normal, who are frequently judged.

I have seen hundreds of patients with chronic pain. For the same intensity of the pain, there is one clear differentiator between a languishing person and another who is thriving—whether that person feels judged or validated. The more judged a person feels, the more overwhelming the pain becomes.

We individually can do so little to help ease other person's pain. One thing we shouldn't do is to worsen their pain by judging them for their struggles.

Today, think of how you can stop judging and start validating and healing at least one person who you know is hurting. Such a commitment will not only help and heal others, but it'll also create words and behaviors you will be proud of when you look back at life.

Day 93

Send success to the heart (so you are kinder) and failure to the head (so you are wiser).

My cousin and her spouse met a new acquaintance named Tina at a party. After a good 20-minute conversation when they were leaving, my cousin invited Tina's family over for dinner. Tina said something to the effect of—"We already have too many friends. Sorry, we can't accommodate one more friend in our life."

My cousin likes candor, but this was candor supersized and insult flavored.

A few years later, life changed for Tina. Her husband died in a corporate jet crash. Tina's finances got out of hand. Many of her erstwhile friends deserted her. She was now looking for help and trying to make new connections.

It is best to never send your success to your head. The world has little compassion when the heady folks come down.

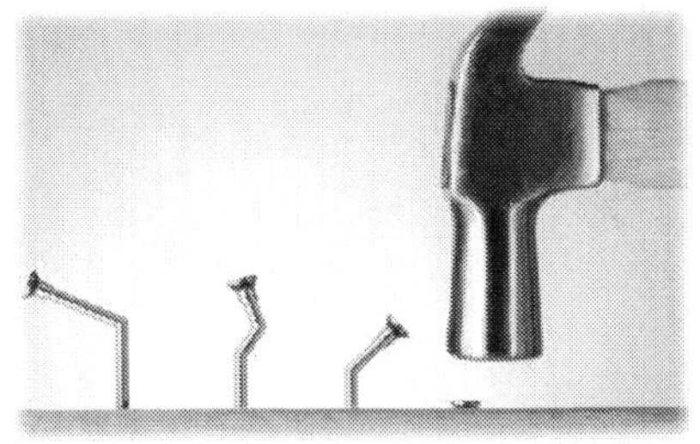

Also, do not send your failure to your heart. Look at failure in totality, surrounded by many moments of success. Failure is just one rung on the success ladder.

I think it's best to send success to your heart, so you remain kind and humble and failure to your head, so you learn and grow because of it.

Think for a moment about the people in your life who remain humble in success and hopeful in failure. What lessons can you learn from these people? Consider connecting with at least one such person today.

Day 94

The people and the principles you serve are your main source of strength. No one living a life of service says at the end of it - "I should have been a little more selfish."

My colleagues in palliative care have asked hundreds of patients their final wishes. No patient do they recall saying I should have been a little more selfish. Most wish they didn't hold back their love. They wish they lived with more courage.

Some of the saddest words I have heard are from a patient who was drugging himself to numb his emotional pain. When I asked him the reason for his hurt, he said, "I divorced the woman I loved."

After two decades of being together, he had stopped seeing her goodness. The good got discounted, the not-so-good got inflated. In fairness to him, many of us tend to discount the good and inflate the bad in the people closest to us, particularly after the novelty of togetherness fades.

But it doesn't have to be this way. We can choose otherwise. We can choose to see those we serve as our source of strength. We can see our morals, our conscience as our pillars. We can choose to seek people who need our help instead of selectively connecting with those who can help us.

If you want to start this change, then think of how serving others has made you stronger. The day every one of us gets convinced that serving others is one of the best ways to serve the self, we will take the first major leap to eliminate inequality and suffering on our planet.

Day 95

Pick the title of your biography—suffering or overcoming. The chapters that fill the book will follow.

The two sides of a coin are separated yet connected. The wall that separates any two rooms also connects the two rooms. Similarly, experiences that might seem the furthest apart, suffering and overcoming, for instance, are also the most connected.

When you look at your past pain, you can choose to focus on the pain or that you overcame it. A focus on the pain depletes energy, while a focus on overcoming creates hope and courage.

The mind's unfortunate instinct is to focus on the suffering, which keeps the suffering alive. Consider making a wiser choice. Just as a patient cured of cancer often sees herself as someone who has beaten or survived cancer (cancer survivor), similarly, if you have overcome a previous suffering, emotional or physical, call yourself a conqueror.

I have met several women whose first name is Hope. I have never met anyone with the first or last name of hopeless, weak shoulders, coward, or ashamed. When you have a choice, why not give yourself a name that fills you with good energy?

One of the ways to feel stronger is to remind yourself of the strengths you have embodied in your previous struggles. Remember such moments today to remain so strong and resilient that suffering itself is fearful of trying to touch you.

Day 96

Grace is like the sunlight, but it is up to us to open the blinds. Close your blinds when the world gets dark. But let the light in when the day seems bright and inviting.

I live in the Midwest. Every summer, we have a few tornado watches and warnings where the protocol is to lower the blinds and close the windows. That's wise and appropriate.

I have lived in cities stricken with war, curfew, or general civil unrest. As a citizen, our response was to shut our windows, close our blinds, and hunker down. That's our reflexive response to an outside threat. When you feel awkward or insulted at a party, you close yourself for self-preservation.

But if the world around you feels safe and inviting, then open the blinds and let the light illuminate every corner. A peculiar reason we don't open ourselves to let the light in is because we sometimes fear happiness. When happy, we fear something terrible might happen.

In my middle school, a teacher created a fear of happiness to control the children. He said, "Kids, the number of times you laugh and cry in your life is the same. Do not laugh for no reason, otherwise you'll have to cry for a good reason." His tactic sadly worked at that time. But his statement had no truth—scientific, emotional, or spiritual.

We need not fear happiness, gratitude, compassion, hope, or courage. A simple way to invite all of these is to think of the many ways you are blessed.

Make a list of at least five of your blessings today, because as I have shared previously, *the more blessed you feel, the more blessed you will feel.*

Day 97

Joy is in caring. The day we start treating rental cars like our own will be the day we will know how to be joyous.

I have driven many rental cars. I must confess I have never felt very connected to them. I fill them with the most economical fuel and am not as careful with keeping them clean. I wouldn't have learned a better way but for a ride with my colleague Bryan.

I ran into Bryan on the flight from San Diego to Minneapolis. Bryan offered to drop me off at my home. Bryan's car had broken down, so he was driving a rental car.

It was clear he took care of this car like his very own. He waited for the engine to warm up before leaving the parking lot, used the brake gently, kept it clutter free, and got the most expensive fuel. I couldn't help but praise him. He said, "It's simple. Right now, this is my car. I want to treat it as if it is mine." That was a valuable and important lesson for me.

Treat every person who comes in your contact with purpose and grace. In fact, it might be a good idea to treat everything, including people, animals, plants, and even things—with purpose and grace.

Think of how you can be extra gentle with everything around you today and every day. Such a disposition will attract good people and good things into your life.

Day 98

Here are the six key ideas we learned this week. Pick the one that makes the most sense to you for today.

- ☐ *Not every pain can be explained by an abnormal MRI scan. Help at least one struggling person feel validated and cared, and not judged and belittled.*
- ☐ *Send success to the heart (so you are kinder) and failure to the head (so you are wiser). Remain humble and inspired, in triumph, as well as failure.*
- ☐ *The people and the principles you serve are your main source of strength. No one living a life of service says at the end of it— "I should have been a little more selfish."*
- ☐ *Pick the title of your biography—suffering or overcoming. The chapters that fill the book will follow. Look at the constraints you have overcome to feel hopeful and strong.*
- ☐ *Grace is like the sunlight, but it is up to us to open the blinds. Close your blinds when the world gets dark. But let the light in when the day seems bright and inviting.*
- ☐ *Joy is in caring. The day we start treating rental cars like our own will be the day we will know how to be joyous.*

I pray you find hope and healing today.

WEEKS 15-16

Theme: Dream big; chase your dreams
Inspiring figure: Martin Luther King Jr.

Learning from his father that segregation and racism are an affront to God's will, MLK Jr. grew with the values of dignity and respect. He organized the Southern Christian Leadership Conference, led the Civil Rights Movement, pursued non-violent activism, and was instrumental in the Civil Rights and Voting Act and ending segregation. He received the Nobel Peace Prize in 1964 at age 35.

Here are three of MLK Jr.'s most inspiring quotes:

"Our lives begin to end the day we become silent about things that matter."

"Darkness cannot drive out darkness: only light can do that. Hate cannot drive out hate: only love can do that."

"Injustice anywhere is a threat to justice everywhere."

Day 99

People who stand strong despite all the rough and tumble give us courage. Keep such people in your thoughts.

Let's say you are putting in all you have got and some more in pursuing a purpose. Along the way, you experience physical assaults, several times you are arrested, your home is bombed, and you nearly die in a stabbing incident. At what point will you throw in the towel and quit?

That's what Martin Luther King, Jr. endured, yet he didn't quit. He kept going and had to pay the ultimate price for his passion.

People like Martin Luther King, Jr. inspire us with the strength of their resolve and the sincerity of their effort.

Think of someone in your life who keeps going despite all the rough and tumble. No one can beat this person's spirit or love of life. Recall a few good qualities about this person or perhaps a story or two of their courage and hard work, and write them in your journal. Keep this person in your thoughts all day long today. Thinking about this resilient person will fill you with hope and courage. It will help you be resilient.

☐

Day 100

The more fruits on a branch, the more it bends. Your humility is a sign of your true accomplishments.

Let's say you went trekking and lost your way. You are alone, hungry, and thirsty. Which tree would you rather run into—an apple tree lush with ripe apples or a very tall date tree with ready-to-eat dates? Barring allergy to one or the other fruit, I would prefer an apple tree.

This is because the fruit on an apple tree is easily accessible. Also, the more fruits on the branch, the more it bends toward the ground, making the fruit even easier to pick.

I love dates too, but the dates on a proud and tall tree are difficult to pick. I will need to play baseball and be good at it to get some dates.

In our life, we can be like apples or dates. The apple people become incrementally humble as they grow. They are wise and very useful for the world. The dates stand inaccessible. They are resourceful, but it's hard for an average person to reach them.

I invite you to be like an apple tree—full of purpose and humility.

Spend a few minutes today thinking about how humility can help you become stronger and more useful. I hope your thoughts will inspire you to spend the day today with greater humility.

Day 101

When one hand is injured, the entire body feels the pain. Our compassionate spirit shares each other's pain. Sharing is healing.

The day you have a bad headache, your entire body hurts and feels inflamed. And the whole body collaborates to heal. Your hands massage and press on the head. Your feet walk over to get the medicine. Your mouth swallows it. Your stomach might get gastritis when absorbing the ibuprofen to comfort the head.

Your hands, feet, mouth, and stomach do not say why should we bother? It's the head that is hurting, not us. They all collaborate because they see themselves as connected. They are part of one, that is you.

I wonder if the same applies to the larger world. Interesting neuroscience research provides a window into this thought.

MRI research findings show that when you see someone you love in pain, your own pain network fires as if you are hurting. Your pain network can't see yourself separate from others. The more connected you feel, the stronger the MRI signals.

This research helps me speculate that healing others' pain might soothe our own pain network. And that's precisely what the researchers are finding. Multiple studies show that helping others activates your reward network and lowers activity in your pain network.

So, think of how you can connect with and help someone who may be hurting. That's one helpful way to soothe your own pain.

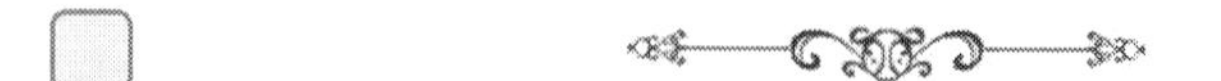

Day 102

If you are struggling with forgiveness, start with forgiving the self. Forgiving others starts with forgiving the self.

Forgiveness can feel like a tall mountain to climb and doesn't feel fair for an egregious hurt. We also worry that by forgiving, we might be making ourselves vulnerable.

As I look at my life, I can think of many situations where I could have been kinder. I would love to revisit those moments, find the people I hurt, knowingly or out of ignorance, and offer an apology.

But those moments are long past; many people have moved on; some are no longer on this planet.

This load feels heavy. Perhaps, the best first step then is to start with forgiving the self.

Self-forgiveness doesn't mean lowering your standards. It is giving yourself the same kindness that you give to others.

Most mistakes happen because of ignorance or misunderstandings, not because of willful misconduct.

Pick a simple mistake of yours. Was it intentional, or did it just happen? Most likely, you didn't intend to hurt anyone. You just didn't know better.

So, today think of how, despite good intentions, mistakes can happen, and forgiveness makes sense. Take the first step toward forgiving the self.

Day 103

Engage people's hearts, not their defenses, particularly with the children and the vulnerable. Validate and love to teach and inspire.

I was once helping an elderly grandma who had been smoking for 50+ years. She had tried everything in the book to quit tobacco but had failed. Then one day, out of the blue, she successfully quit cold turkey.

"What worked," I asked.

She said, "When I leaned forward to kiss my grandson, he took two steps back and said, grandma, you stink. I couldn't take that."

The prematurely aging skin, constant cough, fear of lung cancer, heart disease, stroke, even the risk of early death didn't touch her deep enough. It was her grandson's rejection that she couldn't take.

Emotions are a strong force that pushes us into motion—to make a change. Lasting behavior change is very difficult if you aren't emotionally engaged.

While the grandma may have felt rejected, in this instance, that rejection came from a place of innocence. She knew her grandson wanted to hug her, but something was coming in the way.

In general, one of the best ways to inspire people is to validate them, to help them see the light. Flogging a tired and hungry horse won't make the horse gallop faster. A tired horse needs nourishment which to us humans comes from a healthy dose of uplifting emotions.

So, think of how you can validate and express love toward one person who feels vulnerable today. If we all did that to one person every day, the world would wake up happier every single morning.

Day 104

While we run on different tracks, we are all united by our shared past and future. I, you, and they all belong to a single ancestry tree.

A few years ago, by mistake, I dialed a wrong number. I was in Washington state and reached someone in Chicago. The person on the other side, instead of hanging up, was very courteous. She got interested in knowing me a little. After a few minutes of good conversation, we realized that we were distant relatives.

I am certain that you and I have many common friends. We are all different leaves on the same ancestry tree. Some of us belong to the same branch; others are at a more distant twig.

We have a choice about where we focus. Do we focus on our personal distinct branch or the shared tree? The more we think that we are on a different branch and that each branch competes with the other for the tree's nourishment, the less compassion we have for each other. But if we focus on the tree, which is the deeper reality, we feel connected and compassionate and become more collaborative. We find each other more meaningful.

Perhaps, a good balance is to be aware of both—we are on different branches but the same tree.

So, think of different ways you are connected to others. Think of not only the branch but also the tree. Such thinking is a marker of wisdom that brings us all together. It creates peace in our world.

Day 105

Here are the six key ideas we learned this week. Pick the one that makes the most sense to you for today.

- ☐ *People who stand strong despite all the rough and tumble give us courage. Keep at least one such person in your thoughts today.*

- ☐ *The more fruits on a branch, the more it bends. Your humility is a sign of your true accomplishments. Stay humble.*

- ☐ *When one hand is injured, the entire body feels the pain. Our compassionate spirit shares each other's pain. Sharing is healing. Think of how you can connect with and help someone who may be hurting. That is one helpful way to soothe your own pain.*

- ☐ *If you are struggling with forgiveness, start with forgiving the self. Forgiving others starts with forgiving the self. Focus on your constraints and the good intentions and not just the outcome.*

- ☐ *Engage people's hearts, not their defenses, particularly with the children and the vulnerable. Validate and love to teach and inspire. Think of how you can validate and express love toward one person who feels vulnerable today.*

- ☐ *While we run on different tracks, we all are united by our shared past and future. I, you, and they all belong to a single ancestry tree. Think of different ways you are connected to others.*

I pray you find hope and healing today.

Day 106

Deep within you is a song with lyrics of hope and courage, and music of joy and love. Sing that song today; yours is as melodious as any.

Ask any professor of music, and they will tell you that every person who can speak can sing. Also, even the best singers need ongoing training.

So, let go of the thought that you can't sing. It isn't true. If you put in the effort and find the right teacher, you can create a beautiful melody.

The key, then, is the lyrics. What words will you choose to project? More than ever, the world today is hungry for words that convey hope, courage, joy, love.

When these lyrics fill the garden of your brain, the weeds of self-doubt and hopelessness shrivel.

While the rhythm of the song is important, the choice of your words is even more important. Your language is a living being that changes the energy around you.

It thus makes sense to sing your song today and not spend too much time thinking about the quality of your voice.

Even though I haven't heard your song, I can tell you one thing with full conviction—you sing beautifully when your voice comes from the deepest place in your heart. Ask your brain to sing the song of your heart.

Day 107

The antidotes to fear are logic, action, acceptance, meaning, connection, and faith. Make your own recipe by picking the ideas that make the most sense to you.

At any moment on any given day, you can always find something to fear.

I have struggled with the imposter syndrome—the fear that people will find out I am an intellectual fraud.

I have worried that I will sleep in and miss showing up for work.

Reading about the solar system, I have worried that a large solar flare might one day evaporate our atmosphere.

I have feared a flat tire on a highway.

I have worried about getting rejected in relationships.

I have also wondered about how much pain and suffering awaits me before I leave the planet. And that's just the first few lines of my book of fear.

Not all of these fears have a single generic cure.

I have used logic to overcome imposter syndrome. The logic that I come from a modest background. I have competed in and cleared the exams and haven't been selected because of any family connections.

I have used wake-up alarms with backups to overcome the fear of sleeping in on a workday.

I have had to accept the fear of solar storms. Best to accept something completely uncontrollable.

When faced with a flat tire, I have reframed it by assuming that it may save me from something worse.

I converted my fear of social rejection by dividing my risk—i.e., making positive connections with many good people.

With respect to pain and suffering, I have engaged my faith.

So, think of the different ways you can manage your fears. Perhaps, pick something bothering you and see if one of these—logic, action, acceptance, meaning, connection, and faith—can help you find a more healing perspective. I have a good feeling they will.

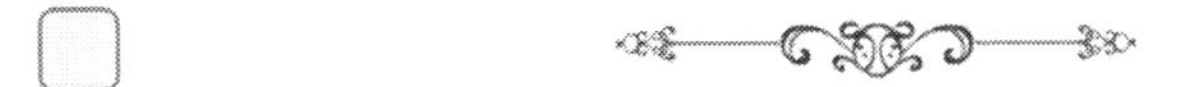

Day 108

Helpful anger is a force of reason that puts energy into peaceful efforts to decrease suffering.

Anger evolved as a force to correct the wrong that could threaten the self.

If a neighboring tribe invades my tribe unprovoked, the anger that helps me mount a counterattack is justified and necessary.

But if I get angry (like mad) at someone who innocently steps on my foot in a crowd or mispronounces my name, then I need help.

In general, anger hurts a relationship with someone, at least temporarily.

A few years ago, I had to display anger to protect a patient. This patient was admitted with bleeding from the colon. The surgeon on call wanted to remove the entire colon.

I was consulted to clear the patient for the surgery, as is customary. I disagreed with the surgeon's decision. I thought, why not find the specific site of the bleed and remove that area instead of the entire colon. That will preserve the important organ and avoid multiple future complications.

An argument ensued. The surgeon yelled at me for interfering in his decision. But in my best conscience, I couldn't yield.

We consulted two independent doctors, who agreed with my suggestion. The bleeder was localized and removed after a colonoscopy. The patient walked out of the hospital without a stoma.

The entire episode hurt my relationship with the surgeon that could never be repaired, but it helped the patient and perhaps taught the surgeon to think more before suggesting major surgeries.

I have no regrets about my decision to get angry at that time. It is because my anger had a purpose that justified its assault on my relationship.

Anger almost always comes with a price tag. The question is does that price justify its benefit. Sometimes it does, often it doesn't. That's a judgment you will have to make.

I hope you have no reason to get angry today.

Day 109

More than fame and fortune, I pray your children feel loved in the world and are skilled at loving themselves.

Just as food comes from all over the world but gets into your body through your mouth, all the positive emotions, feelings of self-worth, and love come to you from all over the world but reach you through one door—your perception of the self.

If our children do not know how to love themselves, they won't feel inspired to work hard, and won't be skilled at taking negative feedback and savor success.

Loving the self entails believing in your intrinsic self-worth. So, what is intrinsic self-worth?

It is your worth that is independent of all your external accomplishments and assets. I might argue no one can measure your intrinsic self-worth, for it is priceless.

The closest you can reach is by thinking about what you mean to the person who loves you unconditionally.

I hope and pray you and your children feel loved unconditionally by at least one person in the world. If you can't think of a person but have a strong anchor in faith, then you can think of the source of your faith loving you unconditionally.

Similarly, I hope and pray you and your children love your own self unconditionally.

Self-love doesn't mean lowering your standards. It means treating yourself kindly. It entails validating yourself for your constraints, looking at yourself with the eyes of someone who loves you for who you are, and measuring yourself for your effort and intentions and not the outcome.

Self-love also knows that every person deserves to have the same self-love as you do.

Consider today writing your hopes for your children and all the worlds' children. I feel many of those hopes will have the key ingredient of our children loving themselves.

Day 110

The day we start living to please the sacred within us will be the day we will stop thinking, saying, or doing anything regrettable and hurtful.

Many offices have computer monitors connected to a central network. The monitors and the keyboard are just a conduit to send information to the central source. Once working on a monitor, I wondered, am I like a monitor, or do I have a hard drive and intentionality within me?

Being just a monitor doesn't inspire me. It hurts my ego. While it absolves me of any responsibility, it also takes away my locus of control and the ability to influence my future. I believe in luck, but I also believe that I can change my future through my actions.

That leads me to believe that the hard drive within me is not only a storehouse of intellect and responsibilities; it also has a priceless spiritual core within it. I believe every person has that spiritual core, the sacred within me and us.

Being aware of your sacred nature can be transformative. Just as you wouldn't want to defile a clean and pristine space, you wouldn't want to treat the sacred within you with impure and hurtful thoughts, words, and actions. So, remind yourself every day of the sacred within you and others.

You can start by thinking today about what makes you priceless. The stronger your belief that you are priceless, the stronger your conviction that everyone around in the world is also priceless, which is a beautiful way to live.

Day 111

You're more likely to win playing for the home team. When you selflessly try to help the world, no matter where you work, you play for the home team.

An interesting research question is—everything else being equal, are you more likely to win when playing for the home team? In general, the answer is yes. In fact, research shows your hormonal response might be more conducive to winning when playing for the home team.

That science gives me an idea for increasing the chance of winning—always play for the home team! But how is that possible given that we belong to a particular school or college, city, state, and country. Here is one suggestion—consider the entire world as your home. Yes, you belong to a city, state, and country, but you also belong to the whole world.

The more you consider yourself a world citizen and think about what is best for the world, the more likely you will think from a zoomed-out global perspective.

With such a disposition, you stop playing to win. You start playing to give it your best. You don't seek accolades; you seek mastery. You aren't competing with anyone except your former self. You are inspired, not to prove to anyone, but to rise to the best you can be—to your satisfaction, to do something meaningful, to serve others.

So, think of how your efforts reach the farthest corner of the world, and the whole world is your home. Such thoughts will give you maturity, your actions a purpose, and take you to master the art that most interests you.

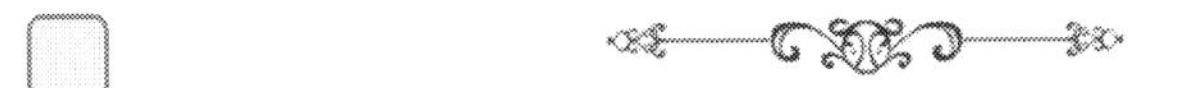

Day 112

Here are the six key ideas we learned this week. Pick the one that makes the most sense to you for today.

- ☐ *Deep within you is a song with lyrics of hope and courage and music of joy and love. Sing that song today; yours is as melodious as any.*
- ☐ *The antidotes to fear are logic, action, acceptance, meaning, connection, and faith. Make your recipe by picking the idea or ideas that make the most sense to you.*
- ☐ *Helpful anger is a force of reason that puts energy into peaceful efforts to decrease suffering. Let your anger be a force of creation and not destruction.*
- ☐ *More than fame and fortune, I pray your children feel loved in the world and are skilled in loving themselves. Children who know how to love themselves will know how to love the world.*
- ☐ *The day we start living to please the sacred within us will be the day we'll stop thinking, saying, or doing anything regrettable and hurtful.*
- ☐ *You're more likely to win playing for the home team. When you selflessly try to help the world, no matter where you work, you play for the home team.*

I pray you find hope and healing today.

WEEKS 17-18

Theme: Live each day with courage and purpose
Inspiring figure: Eleanor Roosevelt

Eleanor Roosevelt wasn't going to be just a symbol of elegance as the first lady. She ran her own press briefings (with only female reporters), took an active part in politics, and became "the President's eyes, ears, and legs." She advocated for the disadvantaged, became the first chair of the UN Commission on Human Rights, and indeed became "the first lady of the world."

Here are three of Roosevelt's most inspiring quotes:

"Do what you feel in your heart to be right—for you'll be criticized anyway."

"No one can make you feel inferior without your consent."

"It isn't enough to talk about peace. One must believe in it. And it isn't enough to believe in it. One must work at it."

Day 113

Courage isn't the lack of fear. Courage is going forward and doing the right thing despite the fear.

So much of Eleanor Roosevelt's life is a story of courage and resilience.

She bounced back from losing her mother and father before she turned ten into becoming a mature young woman committed to social service.

She lost a son before he turned one, but she didn't let that affect her role as a mother and a supportive wife.

When her husband developed polio in 1921, she nursed him while keeping his interest in politics and the world alive. Later, as the longest-serving first lady, she held her own press conference that only female reporters attended.

She actively supported the troops and advocated for the minority, the underprivileged, and the disadvantaged.

The death of her husband, President Roosevelt, didn't slow her resolve to serve. In fact, her role expanded from being the First Lady of the United States to the First Lady of the World.

Over the next 17 years, she actively contributed towards humanitarian causes and tirelessly worked till the very end. No setback and no fear held her progress.

Getting back to courage and fear, do you think fear can help your courage? I feel courage needs a little bit of fear. The courageous use fears to make rational decisions. Their fear keeps them safe instead of limiting them.

Here is the good news. Like many other skills, you can increase your courage. And one of the best ways to do that is to think about the people in your life who are fearless.

So, today, think of a person you know whose life story fills you with courage. Live your day embodying at least one quality that you admire in this person.

Day 114

Four nourishments for the mind: meaningful work, time with loved ones, nature walk, and faith. Pick your selection/s for today!

The other day I was watching my puppy play in the yard. His life is perpetually in the present moment—no thoughts about the past, no concerns about the future.

Not so with us humans.

Our mind carries the load of the endured past and the uncertain future as it tries to navigate the present. That's a lot of loads to lift.

You can help your burdened mind in one or more of three ways: decrease the load, temporarily forget the load, or surrender all the load to a higher power that you completely trust.

Saying no sometimes helps. But when you can't say No, finding meaning in work makes it feel lighter.

Time with loved ones and nature walks are among many approaches that help provide respite from the load.

Faith helps you surrender your hurts and uncertainties to a higher power you trust will know how to heal them.

None of these approaches denies the problem. They recognize that our overloaded, overwhelmed minds need some help, a little respite every once in a while.

So, consider giving yourself a little respite today by thinking and implementing one or more ways you can nourish and rest your mind.

Day 115

It is impossible for two passionate, intelligent people to live in the same space and always agree.

We like people who agree with us or share similarities. They help us feel validated. We also believe that people who are similar to us will more likely approve of us.

So, it is natural for you to want your partner or others to agree with your views. This is understandable but, taken to an extreme, is a recipe for unpleasant arguments. Two intelligent people completely agreeing with each other in every aspect would be very unusual.

Depending on your genetic makeup, childhood experiences, role models, and so much more, you make opinions. Just as your noses, eyes, and hairstyle differ, your brain also has a unique design, as does the content of your thoughts.

So, a mature approach is not only to anticipate but welcome differences. People with a different opinion than yours aren't trying to insult you. They are projecting their independence and intellect. It's a moment to be proud of them.

Further, just as there are different ways to reach DC from New York, you can think about different ways to reach the same goal, with all of them being right in their own way.

In a conversation, I enrich my mind and reach a better conclusion when I focus more on why the other person is right than when I assume he or she is wrong.

So, today think of a few aspects in which you are perfectly fine with yourself and someone close to you being different. Such a disposition will improve your relationship.

Day 116

Meet people as a jet bridge meets the aircraft—with gentleness, purpose, and grace. Together, you will fulfill a greater meaning.

In a meeting, at home, in the neighborhood—we take less than half a second to judge the other person's energy.

And that initial first impression carries considerable weight in influencing how we might relate with the person over the long term.

A good image I carry is that of a jet bridge meeting the aircraft. After the aircraft arrives at the terminal, the jet bridge approaches with a gentle and purposeful movement until they connect for a common purpose.

That gentleness reminds me of how we might meet each other.

A key principle to remember is that you do not have to impress or wow others right away.

Here is relationship 101. *I don't like you because you are so dazzling. I like you because I like myself in your presence.* Help people fall in love with themselves in your presence, and they will like you.

I suggest you plan how you will be extra gentle to the people you meet today. That will help you nurture deeper bonds with many in your lifetime.

Day 117

Use your present wisdom to heal and not judge your past. You didn't know then what you know today.

I wish I knew then what I know today. I would have killed fewer squirrels on the road, would have avoided falling into the ditch, wouldn't have spoken hurtful words, and more.

Our instinct is to judge the actions of our past selves with the knowledge and wisdom we have today. We fail to account that we didn't know then what we know now.

Many, but not all of us, with each passing day, become a little more mature, a little more compassionate and forgiving. Let's use this compassion to heal and not judge the past.

Judging the past keeps us blaming ourselves or someone else. We put labels on people. We trap ourselves and others in these labels.

Healing the past frees us from these labels. Such freedom saves our energy, so we become a source of healing—for ourselves and others.

Help heal today one of yours or someone else's past struggles and mistakes by remembering that you didn't know then what you know today.

Day 118

Meet the grownup hiding in your children and the child hiding in the grownups.

A few years ago, I went to my college reunion. We are all older now, raising families, running businesses, supervising people. A few are already grandparents.

But in the reunion, everybody's mind traveled back 25 years—to our college days. As if a different version of us existed somewhere, waiting for this moment to come alive.

Every grownup has a child that is waiting to be tickled awake. Meeting that playful child helps you experience innocence that we all relish.

It could be as simple as betting which elevator will come first while waiting with others. I have played this little game many times, and almost always, win or lose, we enter the elevator smiling.

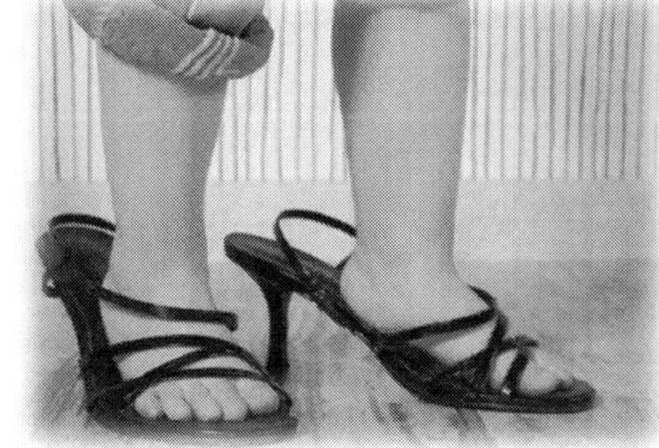

Similarly, every child has a grownup within her. Children are phenomenal at compassion, gratitude, and forgiveness. They also respond wonderfully to humility.

When you approach them with humility treating them like a grownup, they start embodying mature behavior.

Today, notice and admire maturity in the children and innocence in the grownups in your life. Connecting with the child in the adult and the adult in the child will help you get the most out of your connection.

Day 119

Here are the six key ideas we learned this week. Pick the one that makes the most sense to you for today.

- [ ] *Courage isn't the lack of fear. Courage is going forward and doing the right thing despite the fear. Thinking about the courageous people in your life and why the meaning that inspires you is more powerful than the fears that hold you are two simple ways to get more courage.*

- [ ] *Four nourishments for the mind: meaningful work, time with loved ones, nature walk, and faith. Pick your selections for today!*

- [ ] *It is impossible for two passionate, intelligent people to live in the same space and always agree. Accept and honor differences in preferences, opinions, and actions, as long as they don't harm anyone.*

- [ ] *Meet people as a jet bridge meets the aircraft—with gentleness, purpose, and grace. Together, you will fulfill a greater meaning. Plan how you will be extra gentle to the people you meet today.*

- [ ] *Use your present wisdom to heal and not judge your past. You didn't know then what you know today.*

- [ ] *Meet and experience with kindness the grownup hiding in your children and the child hiding in the grownups.*

I pray you find hope and healing today.

Day 120

The past is easier to change than the future. You can change your past by assigning it a different meaning.

I remember my daughter's excitement when she discovered her first loose tooth. She was all grown up now. She now belonged to this exclusive club of children with loose teeth.

The same loose tooth in my sixty-year-old patient isn't the most desirable experience because the meaning is so different.

A loose tooth is a sign of progress and hope in a child but often a sign of loss and poor health in a grownup. Do you see how meaning changes everything?

I believe the past is easier to change than the future because you can assign a different meaning to your past.

Keep in mind, though, that the bigger the loss, the longer it will take to find a comforting meaning.

You can find meaning for a bad haircut or a flat tire but finding meaning for a medical mistake that led to a missed cancer diagnosis might take decades, even a lifetime.

Try and think differently today about a minor past hurt or loss, focusing on finding meaning that provides healing.

Finding meaning in a small hurt might train your mind to think differently about difficult life situations, making you immune to much suffering.

Day 121

Assume today that every blessing is healing you, every loving gesture is touching you, every child is your child, you'll never be alone.

With forest bathing or shinrin-yoku as it is called in Japan, you allow every part of your sensory experience to touch you.

The cool stream, the rough feel of the tree bark, the sunlight breaking through the leaves, the soft touch of dirt, the fragrance of wildflowers—every part of nature's experience helps free your mind from the world of silicon and concrete.

We can try to remain in this calm state all day long. But that's not where I am presently.

My present disposition is excessively self-centric, looking at the personal relevance of every negative news.

From the melting glaciers to an escaped inmate, my mind immediately assesses the event's personal implication. And if I feel there is any way I or someone I hold dear can be affected, I catastrophize.

I can't easily stop catastrophizing, but perhaps I can dilute it by bathing my mind with thoughts and experiences of my choosing.

Let every positive event—a blessing, a good deed, a loving gesture—touch you. Assume that world's every thought of kindness, every child's laughter, every generous action—eventually benefits you. Feel connected with every child in the world.

When you think and feel such, you will always be surrounded by kindness and never be alone.

Let's bathe in kindness today. Look at your life and think of thoughts, experiences, and people who soothe your mind and provide you healing. Like the forest, they are all there. We just have to show up and open our senses to feel their presence.

Day 122

Let's do our part in creating a world where no hurt is left unhealed, and no one is intentionally hurt. Today is a great day to start.

Let's talk about two scenarios.

You are having lunch at a restaurant. A waiter spills some water on your shirt by mistake. He is profusely apologetic.

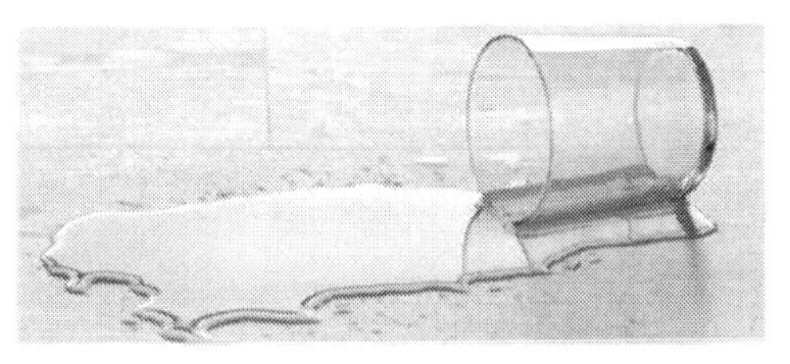

Another situation—You are having lunch at the same restaurant. The same waiter spills the same amount of water on your shirt. But this time, you know it is intentional. The waiter is upset at you for not tipping him well last time. But he didn't provide a good service to you then.

Which of the two situations will anger you more? Perhaps, the second one. Isn't it? Because it has the added punch of intentionality.

Intentionality increases the intensity of the hurt and the resulting anger because we feel singled out and remain concerned that this would happen again. Interestingly, when it comes to hurts, we often feel we are being singled out, even when we are not. But when it comes to blessings, such as someone doing an excellent job for us, we feel that's just who they are, even when they are trying to make it special for us.

I suggest we do the opposite. Take most hurts and insults as unintentional, and every good deed that benefits you as intentional. Consider that everything good in your life was purposefully brought to you, and the good people with you are choosing to be there.

These thoughts will help you create a healed world with fewer intentional hurts.

Day 123

If removing someone from your heart is too painful, then move that person to a different chamber—from the chamber that hosts a loved one or close friend to one that houses an acquaintance or associate.

Your heart has four chambers—two ventricles and the two atria. Here is how it works.

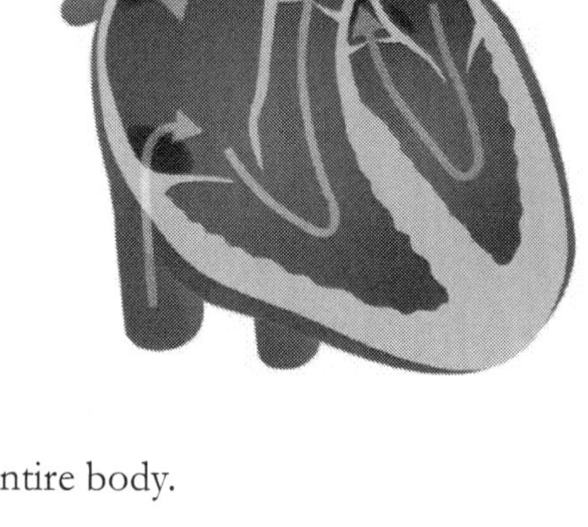

The right atrium receives the blood from the body, sends it to the right ventricle that sends the blood to the lungs.

The lungs clear the blood of carbon dioxide, load it with fresh oxygen and send the blood back to the left atrium.

The blood goes to the left ventricle from the left atrium, that then sends the blood to the entire body.

You don't have to remember all these details! Just know that all parts of the heart are vital, but perhaps the most important part that we want to keep strong and flexible is the left ventricle.

Now, this doesn't mean that when we say someone is in my heart, they are in our left ventricle! Of course, we mean they are in our metaphoric hearts.

I like to keep the people closest to me in my metaphoric left ventricle.

But when these people serially disappoint me, I move them to a different chamber of my heart, maybe the right atrium, hoping they will find back their spot in time.

I find this approach a little more practical than completely removing them from my heart, which I did in the past.

Our relationships are dynamic. Even the closest relationships have transactional and adversarial moments.

Most close relationships—among friends and relatives—relate to how worthy, loved, and respected we feel in others' presence.

And none of us can meet the world's expectations every single day. So, disappointments are bound to happen.

I suggest we limit our expectations, recognize others' constraints, and when hurt, instead of giving up on people, redefine our relationships to maintain them (i.e., move them to a different chamber of our heart).

See if this is something you can give a try today.

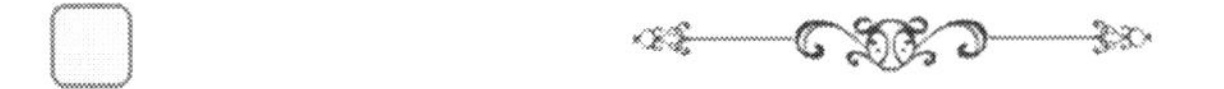

Day 124

As you read these words, 30,000 people in the world are thinking of taking their life. Feel grateful and compassionate in honor of those who can't access these feelings today.

No matter how blessed we are, unless we choose to remind ourselves of our blessings, the positive feelings fade in our minds.

This is because of a simple quirk—our mind by design discounts the good and inflates the bad.

I have met many people who are all stressed out because of a small crack in the concrete pavement in their second home. I wish to remind them that millions, perhaps billions of people in the world, do not have a decent first home.

Once I was struggling with personal, trivial worries—research grants, unpublished papers, rejected insurance claims, and more.

In the middle of all this, while walking to a coffee shop, I saw a child, about ten years old, in a wheelchair. He looked undernourished, his head was shaven, and he had a tube running up his nose.

Seeing that child reset my mind, reminding me that the problems I am worried about are so little in the context of what many others are facing.

People who get all riled up from a simple thing could be because they are born with a biological predisposition to ruminate, dwell on the negative, and feel sad and anxious. It's not anyone's mistake. It's a pure biological predisposition, such that a rejection or a loss that others may disregard takes away all their hope.

At any moment, tens of thousands of people in the world are struggling with such predisposition.

Let's feel compassionate today for every person who feels sad—

either because of their life's situation or because of the way their brain processes adversity, often both.

Feel also grateful if you aren't overwhelmed with personal adversity and thus have space in your mind for compassion.

I pray you always keep compassion and gratitude in your mind and your heart.

☐ 

Day 125

Forces that hurt our hearts are stronger than ones that break our bones. A tree that resists 70 mph winds can fall to wood beetles that hollow it from inside.

I have had my share of computer viruses. Every time my hard drive would crash, I used to wonder, how can this little code cause so much destruction?

Well, that little thing has a penchant for replicating itself, and once it multiplies a billion times or more doesn't remain so little. That's how subtle becomes stronger than gross.

An infested tree is attacked from the inside, not by one or ten but hundreds or thousands of beetles that can destroy its wood, hollowing the tree from its inside.

Thoughts or words that hurt our self-worth multiply in our heads. A single thought connects with many other similar thoughts, multiplies itself, and takes over our brain, activating the stress pathways, releasing adrenaline and steroids, raising blood pressure and heart rate, and causing a general increase in wear and tear.

Forces that hurt our hearts are thus often stronger than the ones that break our bones.

Here is the truth. The initial negative thought is bound to come to your mind. It will be superhuman to eliminate that from happening.

Your strength is in preventing it from multiplying through building a robust psychological immune system.

Strong attention, reframing with gratitude, compassion, meaning, forgiveness, acceptance, meditation, and faith are a few strategies that can help.

Today, think of the different ways you can help your mind become stronger.

Once you are strong from the inside, you will also become strong from the outside.

Day 126

Here are the six key ideas we learned this week. Pick the one that makes the most sense to you for today.

- [ ] *The past is easier to change than the future. Assign it a different meaning, and your past will feel different.*
- [ ] *Assume today that every blessing is healing you, every loving gesture is touching you, every child is your child, you'll never be alone.*
- [ ] *Let's do our part in creating a world where no hurt is left unhealed and no one is intentionally hurt. A great way to start is to assume that everything good in your life was purposefully brought to you.*
- [ ] *If removing someone from your heart is too painful, then move that person to a different chamber—from the chamber that hosts a loved one or close friend to one that houses an acquaintance or associate.*
- [ ] *As you read or hear these words, 30,000 people in the world are thinking of taking their life. Feel grateful and compassionate in honor of every person who feels sad and can't easily access gratitude and compassion.*
- [ ] *Forces that hurt our hearts are stronger than ones that break our bones. A tree that resists 70 mph winds can fall to wood beetles that hollow it from inside. Once you are strong from the inside, you will also become strong from the outside.*

I pray you find hope and healing today.

WEEKS 19-20

Theme: Think big, forgive, be patient
Inspiring figure: Nelson Mandela

As a young man, Nelson Mandela was profoundly touched by the despair he saw in the eyes of the South African youth. Through diplomacy and non-violent activism, he secured freedom for his country at tremendous personal cost, including jail time for 27 years. One of his most significant contributions was his commitment to forgiveness. No wonder he dropped early his first name, Rolihlala, which means "troublemaker" in the Xhosa language!

Here are three of Mandela's most inspiring quotes:

"Do not judge me by my successes, judge me by how many times I fell down and got back up again."

"May your choices reflect your hopes, not your fears."

"If you talk to a man in a language he understands, that goes to his head. If you talk to him in his language, that goes to his heart."

Day 127

One of the best ways to prepare for forgiveness is to think about those who were hurt worse than you but still chose to forgive.

I truly admire dogs for their forgiveness skills.

Once, when I overslept my alarm and didn't take my dog Simba out early in the morning, I fully expected him to yell at me.

But when he saw me, the little guy just lovingly wagged his tail, as if saying, "Don't worry. I understand. I am sure you must be busy!"

By comparison, when I failed to wake up a close relative first thing in the morning, they weren't instantly forgiving.

Over the years, I have found that forgiveness is a skill like any other—swimming, biking, cooking.

A unique human challenge is that the revenge instinct is stronger than the passion for forgiveness. So, how do I make forgiveness the more dominating force?

Two ideas work:

One, think about someone who was hurt worse than you yet chose to forgive.

Nelson Mandela spent 27 years of his life in prison under challenging conditions. Yet, he forgave his jailors who had hurt him. His forgiveness helped bring reconciliation and unity to his country.

Two, dedicate your forgiveness to someone you hold dear who is struggling. Something like, may the goodness that comes from my forgiveness help my niece Laura who struggles with severe migraines.

Even though it might be difficult to scientifically prove if Laura will be helped, your commitment to her will make forgiveness easier.

So, think about the kindest, most forgiving people you know who themselves experienced significant adversities, and connect your forgiveness with a purpose close to your heart.

These two ideas will help you find an easier path to forgiveness.

Day 128

If you fall, choose to rise higher than where you fell from. Often, the only time we get to rise is when we have fallen.

A few months ago, I got carryout dinner for my family and was driving back home. It was drizzling, just past the sunset. I was on a straight road into which many side streets were merging.

Suddenly I heard a loud bang as if a bomb had gone off in my car. My car was hit on the driver's side by someone who made a sudden left turn in front of me. Both our cars got dragged to the curb, barely stopping before hitting the slope that could have propelled us onto the highway.

I was deemed at no fault and wasn't penalized for the accident. But it changed my driving habits—in three phases.

In phase one, I was anxious and paranoid. I assumed everyone on the road was out to hit me. Thankfully this phase lasted only a few days.

In phase two, I resolved to overcome my anxiety and become the world's best driver. I began noticing every single yellow and white line, strictly followed the speed limit, and more. That phase lasted for about three months.

Finally, phase three is where I am a more cautious and engaged driver than ever, but not obsessively. The accident has definitely helped my driving.

Just as a bouncy ball jumps higher than the level from which it is thrown, we can choose to rise because we fell, excel because we didn't do well, and fabulously succeed because we failed. That's the resilience model.

Recall instances today where you or someone you know rose because you or they fell.

I hope and pray that you never fall, but if you ever do, you rise higher than ever before.

Day 129

Trying to prove that you are right may be a wasted effort. A much better use of your energy is to prove that you are kind.

In a resilience workshop, I was once talking to a teacher who was highly stressed before the start of the school year.

"I want to make sure I pay attention to all the details, that the students and parents who come for the orientation feel that I have it all together," she said.

I thought, as a parent, whenever I go to those orientations, I am more focused on getting to know the teacher—how kind she is, will she be patient with my child—and less focused on if she knows all the forms.

I shared this thought with her. While she is trying to prove she knows all the details, parents and students, who are themselves nervous, are trying to see how patient and kind she is.

Realizing that most students and parents are struggling when they see her, she shifted her energy.

Instead of trying to show her brilliance and competence, she worked on her kindness and patience.

It turned out to be the easiest and most efficient start to her school year.

Think of how you can show kindness in words and actions. Remember that competence follows kindness. The kinder you are, the more competent you will become.

And of course, gift to yourself the same kindness and patience today that you gift to the world.

Day 130

Let go of judging someone today who is sensitive and easily gets hurt. He may be stuck in a difficult situation that he can't tell.

Do you wonder why some people seem to flow with the same stressful situation that might collapse the other person? It is related to three strikes.

The first strike is your genetic predisposition.

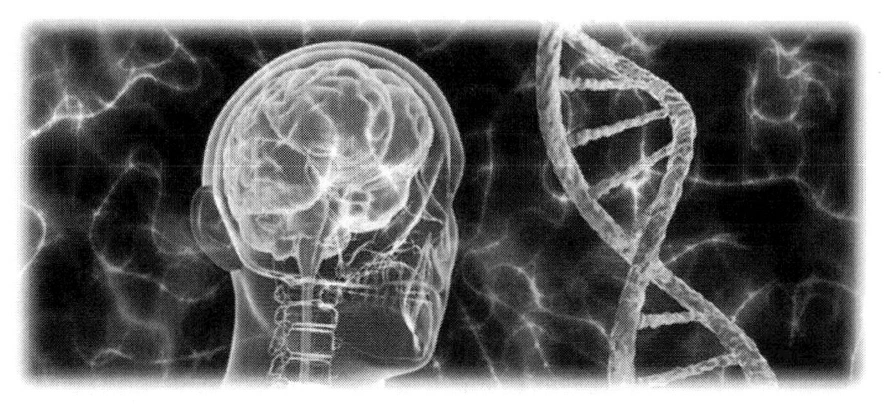

Many genes work together to influence your brain's structure and the level of neurotransmitters in your brain. For example, people who are genetically predisposed to produce less oxytocin struggle with feeling and expressing gratitude.

Better to call someone ungrateful as a person struggling with low oxytocin instead of blaming them.

The second strike is childhood adversity—both in poverty-stricken and affluent neighborhoods.

Keep in mind that while material scarcity often predisposes to emotional poverty, affluence doesn't guarantee emotional thriving.

The third strike is the stress level in adult life.

Again, stress is present in both affluent and impoverished

neighborhoods. The cause of stress might be different. But the body's response is the same. And we are more likely to judge the wealthier people who get stressed out.

So, think today of someone you know who gets easily stressed. Instead of judging that person, assume that they are struggling because of vulnerable genotype, adverse childhood experiences, and a boatload of stressors.

Such thoughts will make it easier for you to be kind.

Day 131

Patience improves your mood, decreases your risk of accidents, heart disease, and early death, and increases career success.

Long traffic lights, slow websites, inching traffic, delayed flights, people who take 48 minutes to come to the point—they all test my patience. And my impatience isn't predictable.

I am more patient in certain situations and with certain people. For example, the day I am getting late for work, I so wish my microwave could warm the cereal in two seconds. Otherwise, I don't mind the sixty-second countdown.

I have realized that I don't enjoy moments and days when I am less patient. Research confirms this experience.

Impatience worsens mood, increases the risk of accidents, hurts physical health, increases risk of heart attack, impedes career success and relationships, and even may cause early death.

Research also shows that with practice, you can build your patience muscles. Here are three ways of doing it:

1. Find greater meaning in the tedious task,

2. Couple a boring task with something interesting such as playing music while loading the dishwasher; and

3. Develop a skill to shift your attention to something interesting (such as noticing all the different hairstyles while waiting in the checkout line at the grocery store).

I suggest you pick one or more ideas from above and then think about one situation in which you are most impatient. Commit to extra patience today during that situation by applying your preferred idea or ideas.

I pray you are able to lower your stress, find greater happiness, better your health, and improve your relationships by becoming more patient.

Day 132

Let your personal pain help you become compassionate toward others' pain. Suffering that inspires kindness is a force of transformation.

I haven't had the healthiest self-worth for the longest time.

Most compliments ricochet back while critiques endure like stuck with superglue.

Sometimes I see this predisposition as a gift because it keeps me dissatisfied, which gives me the energy to push myself to remain useful.

Another benefit is that my self-worth issues make me sensitive about not hurting anyone else's self-worth. My apologies if it sounds like I am gloating a bit here.

In general, people who have gone through a struggle either become sensitive to others' struggles or become numb and insensitive.

When struggling with a life challenge, the last thing you want to hear is, "Come on, be strong. I have been through worse and did just fine." Shaming doesn't help, while validation works like magic.

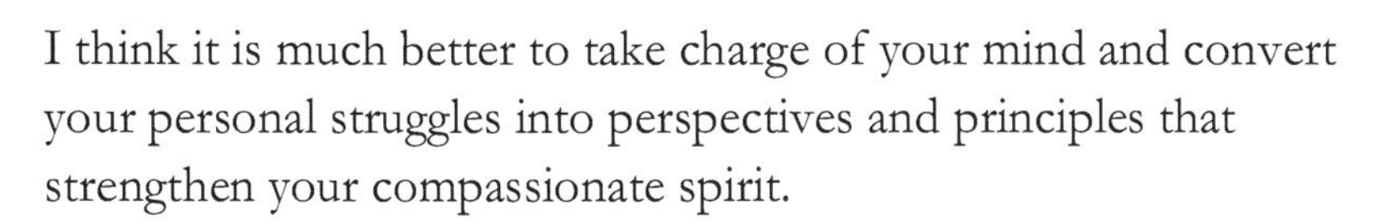

I think it is much better to take charge of your mind and convert your personal struggles into perspectives and principles that strengthen your compassionate spirit.

For today, think of ways to help someone overcome a struggle similar to a difficulty you experienced in the past. Even thinking and planning such a kind action might be enough to lift your day.

Day 133

Here are the six key ideas we learned this week. Pick the one that makes the most sense to you for today.

- ☐ *One of the best ways to prepare for forgiveness is to think about those who were hurt worse than you but still chose to forgive. Thinking about them will give you peace and make forgiveness easier.*
- ☐ *If you fall, choose to rise higher than where you fell from. Often, the only time we get to rise is when we have fallen. Think of one weakness that you can convert to strength today.*
- ☐ *Trying to prove that you are right may be a wasted effort. A much better use of your energy is to prove that you are kind. Find creative ways to be kind today.*
- ☐ *Let go of judging someone today who is sensitive and easily gets hurt. He may be stuck in a difficult situation that he can't tell. Perhaps he is struggling because of a vulnerable genotype and adverse childhood experiences that he has forgotten.*
- ☐ *Patience improves your mood, decreases your risk of accidents, heart disease, and early death, and increases career success. Commit to greater patience today during a situation where you are likely to be impatient.*
- ☐ *Suffering that inspires kindness is a force of transformation. Think of ways you can help someone overcome a struggle you had in the past. Let your personal pain help you become compassionate toward others' pain.*

I pray you find hope and healing today.

Day 134

The better your binoculars, the more scars you'll see on the moon. The closer you get to know someone, the more flaws you'll find in them.

One traumatic experience that I now avoid is looking at my reflection in one of those magnifying mirrors. I end up seeing all the scars, dents, and spots I didn't know existed on my face.

When you look at the full moon with bare eyes, it looks gorgeous. But the moment you put on a pair of binoculars, you see all the scars. This is the binocular effect, which often happens in relationships.

The more we get to know people, the more imperfections we discover. On top of that, our mind's instinct is to discount the good and inflate the bad, which doesn't help.

Because of the combined influence of the binocular effect, loss of novelty, discounting the good, and inflating the bad, our relationships fade with time. You can choose not to let that happen to you.

Adjust for the binocular effect by knowing that the moon's scars aren't the moon's fault. The moon has been pelted by rocks for a long time. Similarly, people's imperfections are often because of previous hurts endured over a lifetime.

Knowing this, focus on the good in others, notice similarities with you, and think of ways to optimize your expectations. These little practices can do wonders to maintain and heal your bonds.

Consider taking the first step today by lowering expectations and adjusting for the binocular effect with one person who may have annoyed you previously.

Day 135

We are kinder toward those we find similar to us. Finding similarities warms up our feelings toward another person.

In a research study, half of the university students were told that they shared their date of birth with someone who was struggling, and the other half weren't told the same. When tested for compassion, the group that believed they shared the date of birth had much more compassionate feelings.

Thucydides said of the Greek plague, "*Yet it was in those who had recovered from the plague that the sick and the dying found most compassion.*"

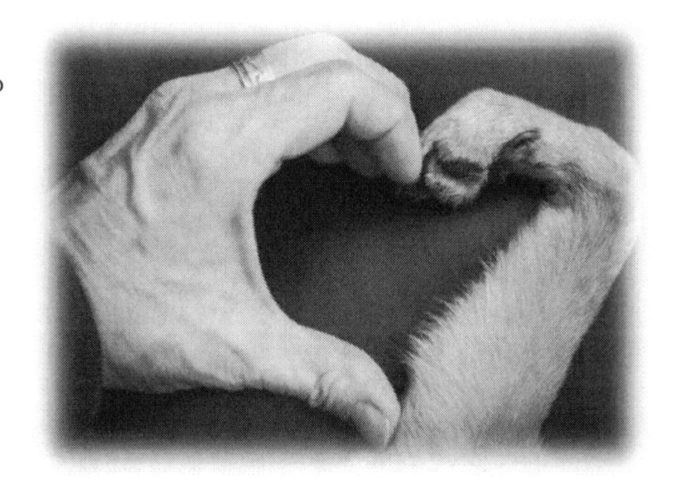

We like people who are similar to us. We feel less threatened by them. They help us feel validated and lift our self-worth.

The truth is you share more similarities than differences with every person on the planet. Often, it's just a matter of trying and finding out for yourself.

So, today think of someone who annoys you. Write as many things as you can (but at least five) that are common between you and that person. It will help you become a little kinder toward that person, and also kinder toward yourself.

Day 136

Four ideas for today—savor your food 10% more, walk 10% more, meet loved ones and friends with 10% more energy, and keep 10% more hope.

A ship that travels a thousand miles, if it makes a one-degree change in its direction, would reach an entirely new location. Today, let's try to make one small sustainable change.

I will share four ideas in each of which I invite you to enhance your presence and experience by 10%. Pick the one that makes the most sense to you and apply it in your life.

One, research the history of one food item you will eat in the next meal. Knowing your food better will help you savor it a bit more.

Two, increase your physical activity by a little. Modify one sedentary activity in your day so you are more physically active during that time.

Three, meet your loved ones for the first two seconds as if you haven't seen them for a long time, with just a little extra presence.

And four, feel a little more hopeful by thinking of all your past accomplishments and the people who believe in you.

So, think of what you want to do 10% more today—savoring food, walking more, meeting loved ones with greater energy, and feeling more hopeful.

Take the first step in implementing that change at your earliest convenience.

☐ 

Day 137

We swim in an ocean of uncertainty. Just as fish can't afford to be afraid of water, we can't afford to be fearful of uncertainty.

I remember those early years of driving in the pre-GPS days. My driving skills were a little raw, so I stayed in the right lane to not slow down the traffic. The right lane would eventually become an exit lane, and my tardy reactions won't let me move leftward.

I would take the undesired exit and end up in an unfamiliar cul-de-sac. The drives were stressful, and not uncommonly, I would be late by 30 minutes for my meeting or dinner or wherever I was going.

Frustrated, one day, I decided to change my expectation. I started adding 30-minutes to my commute as "getting lost time" until my driving skills improved. That adjustment removed the time pressure making my drives much more pleasurable.

You have a choice in how you tackle uncertainty—flow with it or fight. Some uncertainties are worth fighting, but many call you to adapt to the situation.

I call uncertainty the X factor and include it in all my expectations. Sometimes the uncertainty is small such as in ordering a pizza, but other times it's large, such as the stock market's direction. Keeping the X factor in the equation has decreased my disappointments.

So, of all the myriad uncertainties, think of one or more you are comfortable accepting today, if only for the next few hours. The fewer uncertainties in your mind, the greater peace in your life.

Day 138

Sometimes the best of people, despite all the hard work, experience failure. Measure yourself not by your success but by the values you embody.

I have worked with hundreds of physicians over the last four decades. Among all of them, one physician stands out in my mind.

He was my mentor in New Delhi, a perfect combination of compassion and brilliance.

Every day was a flow experience for him, absorbed as he was in listening to stories, diagnosing problems, teaching, and healing. Extremely humble and with an astute clinical sense, he was destined for greatness.

But a bad argument about an ethical issue with a person in power led to a few wrong words written in his file. His career came to a standstill.

Even though his work has progressed through sheer grit, and he has contributed meaningfully, I feel the world failed to benefit from his full potential.

I am sure you know one or more good, hardworking people who have everything going for them, but they don't taste success as they deserve.

In your control are your effort, intentions, and values. But no one can guarantee success as defined by the world. I believe, as long as you gave the best possible effort with good intentions, and lived and performed by your values, you have succeeded.

So, today think of the most important values that guide your life and try your best to live your day with those values.

Call this day productive if you are able to do that, no matter how much or how little you accomplish through the day.

Day 139

A hospital janitor saves as many lives as a doctor. Honor the meaning (how one serves the world), not just the means (what one does).

A janitor colleague of mine was once asked to describe her work. Her response: "I save lives."

And she is right. She cleans the hospital rooms of nasty infections, keeping patients safe.

Our society doesn't reward us for the meaning we fulfill. If that were the case, an elementary school teacher would be earning more than a baseball player or investment banker.

If you look at history, a thousand years ago, trading spices could have made you a millionaire, but speculating on stocks might do the same today. So, measuring your work by its dollar rewards would be inaccurate.

Instead, a more accurate valuation is based on the people you serve and the values you embody. The rewards aren't in your control, but you have much greater control over living your values and the desire to serve.

So, today think of the profound importance of the work of one person you know who isn't as celebrated for what they do.

The more you celebrate and honor their meaning, the more they will honor yours.

☐ 

Day 140

Here are the six key ideas we learned this week. Pick the one that makes the most sense to you for today.

- ☐ *The better your binoculars, the more scars you'll see on the moon. The closer you get to know someone, the more flaws you'll find in them. Consider taking the first step to improving your relationship today by lowering expectations with one person who may have annoyed you.*

- ☐ *We are kinder toward those we find similar to us. Finding similarities warms up our feelings toward another person. Write as many things as you can, but at least five, that are common between you and a person who annoys you.*

- ☐ *Four ideas for today—savor your food 10% more, walk 10% more, meet loved ones and friends with 10% more energy, and keep 10% more hope.*

- ☐ *We swim in an ocean of uncertainty. Just as fish can't afford to be afraid of water, we can't afford to be fearful of uncertainty. Of all the myriad uncertainties, think of one or more you are comfortable accepting, if only for today.*

- ☐ *Sometimes the best of people, despite all the hard work, experience failure. Measure yourself not by your success but by the values you embody.*

- ☐ *A hospital janitor saves as many lives as a doctor. Honor the meaning (how one serves the world), not just the means (what one does). Today think of the profound importance of the work of at least one person you know who isn't as celebrated for what they do.*

I pray you find hope and healing today.

WEEKS 21-22

Theme: Aim high and believe in yourself
Inspiring figure: Joan of Arc

A humble warrior, steadfast in her resolve and guided by divine visions, Joan of Arc, at 16-years of age, launched her mission to free France from foreign forces. She completed that mission at age 17. Not receiving the support that she deserved, she left the planet too soon—as a teenager. About 500 years later, she was canonized and is the patron saint of France.

Here are three of Joan of Arc's most inspiring quotes:

"I am not afraid... I was born to do this."

"Act, and God will act."

"One life is all we have, and we live it as we believe in living it. But to sacrifice what you are and to live without belief, that is a fate more terrible than dying."

Day 141

Seek not a life free of adversity. That wish won't be granted. Seek a life of strength to face and fight the adversity and wisdom to grow because of it.

I cannot think of a more driven, accomplished, and courageous teenager than Joan of Arc.

Guided by a divine vision where she saw herself as the savior of France, Joan led a successful assault on foreign forces and, in a short time, freed France.

Unfortunately, in the next battle, she got injured, was captured by enemy forces, and eventually tried for Heresy. Sadly, she died at the stake in front of a crowd of 10,000 people.

Twenty-five years after her death, she was found innocent of all charges and was declared a martyr. She was later canonized and is the patron saint of France.

Struggles, small or large, decorate every person's life. The bigger the struggle you overcome, the more timeless your legacy.

No one likes losses, regrets, or hurts—but it's impossible to avoid them completely. In fact, a life without losses, regrets, or hurts will also likely be unaccomplished.

A much better ask is to have the strength to face and fight the adversities. It is these fights that join in building your resilience.

So, today think of a few examples from your life where a short-term adversity bolstered your strength and helped you in the long term.

Perhaps, this thought might decrease your fear of future adversities and inspire you to embrace them with a more open heart.

Day 142

Remember a past selfless action of yours and try to do something similar to that action.

On any given day, we are neither wholly selfless nor totally selfish. We do a mix of things that involve taking care of the self and helping others.

Most actions that help others occur in the context of our defined roles—as a parent, professional, colleague, neighbor, and more.

But at times, we act purely out of the goodness of our hearts.

When you stop to help someone find directions in the downtown maze, when you join others in helping push a car stuck in mud or snow, when you add an extra dollar to your carryout bill to support a charity, when you write a five-star review for a book or a product—you are being selfless, expecting nothing in return.

Interestingly, your selfless actions are the ones that provide the greatest help to the self.

Your previous selfless actions help you in three ways –

- They help you feel happier.
- They lift your self-worth.

- And very importantly, they prompt you to repeat your selfless actions.

The more you remind yourself of your goodness, the better a person you become. Remembering previous selfless actions thus puts you in a nice positive feedback loop of positivity.

So, start with thinking about a previous selfless and kind action of yours. Perhaps that thought might prompt you to repeat your kindness, lifting your day and that of someone else.

Day 143

Personal hurts multiply when you revisit them too often; personal hurts heal when you attend to others who are hurting.

Asking a dog to stop sniffing, a dolphin to stop playing, a lion to stop hunting, a tree to stop growing, or a toddler to stop toddling will be impractical. These are ingrained instincts within each one of them that are difficult to reverse.

Similarly, we have a pain network in the brain that processes both physical and emotional pain. The pain network's job is to scan the world, the body, and the mind for anything hurtful that could threaten your physical and emotional being. Expecting your pain network to remain quiet and suppressed is impractical.

But here is what you can do. You can choose the pain you focus on and how you react to it. When your pain network gets busy attuning with and healing other people's pain, then it leaves you with a sense of uplifted self-worth.

Lacking that focus, the pain network gets busy with personal pain, real or imagined.

So, friend, pain we will experience. There is no escaping that. But you have a choice in which pain draws your greatest attention—your personal pain, or someone else's pain. Focusing on others' pain with a desire to heal will help you heal and put you in an upward spiral of life.

Today is a great day to start by thinking and planning how you can personally help heal someone you know is hurting.

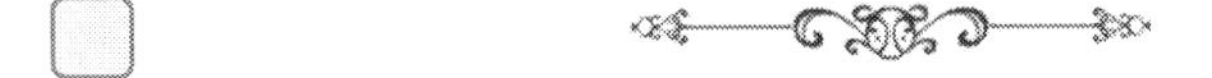

Day 144

Most people struggle with self-worth and self-doubt. One of the most precious gifts you can give to others is to help them believe in themselves.

I was once leading a retreat of about 25 resilience trainers. These are professionals who have committed their careers to study and teach resilience.

Halfway into the retreat, I asked them to imagine meeting their sixteen-year-old self. "If you have a minute with your younger self, what words will you say to help and inspire her?"

The universal answer was, "Believe in yourself. You are enough. It will all work out."

Next, I asked them to say a few words of comfort and inspiration to their present self.

The answer was the same, "Believe in yourself. You are enough. It will all work out."

Keep in mind, I was talking to all the resilience experts. They struggled with self-worth as a teenager and still had the same struggles as a grownup.

This realization has helped simplify my every relationship. Every person I meet I assume has self-worth and self-doubt issues.

Consider using this insight in your life. As you meet people today, remember that every person you are meeting feels vulnerable, to a small or larger degree.

Think of ways you can help others feel worthy and confident. If you remember this simple rule, all your interactions through the day, with others and yourself, will be at least a little more affiliative than otherwise.

Day 145

Love shines the brightest in the hearts purified by wisdom borne of suffering. Let your struggles purify and not demoralize you.

Once I was dining with a loved one who had nuts and egg allergies. We were naturally concerned about food safety.

The head chef, a conscientious and professional gentleman, reassured us. Before he left, he said, "Don't worry. My younger one has a bunch of allergies. I know exactly what to do." Those words comforted us more than anything else.

We trust and like people who understand us, who we can relate to.

The other day, I was thinking about all the good people in my life with whom I would love to sit down and have a pleasant conversation. Every single person in that group had one thing in common—they had experienced struggles.

I find people who have struggled in the past, particularly if they used those struggles to become wiser, kinder, and more loving, much more relatable than someone born with a silver spoon in the mouth who was shielded from every storm and wind gust.

Our struggles can either demoralize us and put us down or inspire us and make us stronger. Try your best to look at step backs as commas in the middle of a sentence and not the final period at the end of the book.

A few ideas that can help you flow better with adversity are –

For smaller struggles such as spilled milk, ask yourself—will it matter in 5 years? If not, then it isn't worth more than five minutes of your time.

For moderate struggles such as a flat tire—focus on what went right within what went wrong. It is just a flat tire and not a totaled car.

For real bad struggles such as severe illness—put your energy and thoughts into what is actionable, seek support from friends, loved ones, and competent professionals, and remember your faith.

I hope you never have to face struggles, particularly the real bad ones. But the better prepared you are, the more effective you will be in converting your struggles into your moments of growth.

Today, think of different ways your struggles have helped you rise. Such thinking can serve as a starting point in your resilient transformation.

Day 146

Help yourself by helping someone who has no ability to repay you. That's how we all were lifted one day.

Every interaction in the world entails an energy exchange. We get paid for the work we do proportionate to the value that society assigns to our work. This value is a moving target based on your expertise, the risks you take, and competition.

For example, if most of the plumbers in your town choose to become coders and you have only one plumber left, then his fee will very likely double or triple until some fresh plumbers move in.

In many jobs, the energy you get for the work isn't in dollars. It is more subtle. Taking care of a baby, for example—changing the diaper, giving her a bath, feeding, holding her close to you—the return energy is satisfaction and love.

Similarly, while many can compensate in kind for what you do, not everyone can. However, you still get something in return. What you get is gratitude, satisfaction, happiness, self-worth, better health, and even longer life.

Most jobs in the world can't promise all of these gifts. Don't you think then it's a good idea to do something for someone who has no ability to repay you?

So, plan on helping someone who cannot reciprocate. The subtle return gifts you will get can't be measured in dollars. They are immeasurably precious.

Day 147

Here are the six key ideas we learned this week. Pick the one that makes the most sense to you for today.

- ☐ *Seek not a life free of adversity. That wish won't be granted. Seek a life of strength to face and fight the adversity and wisdom to grow because of it. This thought might help decrease your fear of future hardships and inspire you to embrace them with a more open heart.*

- ☐ *Remember a past selfless action of yours and try to do something similar to that action. The more you remind yourself of your goodness, the better a person you will become. Remembering a previous selfless action puts you in an upward spiral of life.*

- ☐ *Personal hurts multiply when you revisit them too often; personal hurts heal when you attend to others who are hurting. Think and plan how you can personally help heal someone else who you know is hurting.*

- ☐ *Most people struggle with self-worth and self-doubt. One of the most precious gifts you can give to others is to help them believe in themselves. Think of ways you can help others feel worthy and confident.*

- ☐ *Love shines the brightest in the hearts purified by wisdom borne of suffering. Think of different ways your struggles have helped you rise. Let your struggles purify and not demoralize you.*

- ☐ *Help yourself by helping someone who has no ability to repay you back. That's how we all were lifted one day. The subtle return gifts you get by helping someone can't be measured in dollars. They are immeasurably precious.*

I pray you find hope and healing today.

Day 148

Try your best not to quit. But if you feel spent, nothing wrong with taking a break.

Think of the last time you drove 200 miles on a highway. What did you see on the windshield at the end of the drive? Lots of dead bugs, isn't it?

The same happens to the brain at the end of a long day. The brain accumulates lots of extra chemicals called neurotransmitters at the junction of the neurons.

These rogue neurotransmitters prevent efficient neuronal communication, which translates to the feeling of fatigue, lack of focus, and general languishing.

If you have felt wiped out by the end of the day some days, it is because your brain is lush with these extra neurotransmitters.

What clears your brain of these chemicals? A good rest lowers your central adrenaline level, which in turn opens the channels to clear the brain. Rest is the time when the brain's garbage trucks clear the brain of its unhealthy trash. Hence, rest isn't a passive state. Rest actively rejuvenates your brain.

The cornfields must rest in the winter for them to be productive in the spring. I feel one of the best ways not to quit is to give yourself some well-deserved rest every so often.

An excellent first step would be to convince your mind to take it easy for a bit by writing down some of the benefits of adding slow moments to your day.

I hope you feel rested today.

Day 149

Recognize that majority of suffering in the world is invisible. This recognition might help you default to kindness.

A few years ago, my wife Richa and I were watching a local cultural program. One dancer who was performing solo, let's call her Asha, stole everyone's heart.

With a charming smile, good energy, and graceful moves, she looked like she was in flow. I remarked how well Asha was dancing.

Richa replied, "Do you know Asha came back last night from an overseas trip. She has hardly slept for 48 hours. Her mother unexpectedly passed away a week ago. She was only 65. Asha was very close to her mother."

I was shocked to hear that. Asha's face belied the pain she was carrying in her heart.

Just as scientists believe only 5% of the matter and energy is visible to us and a full 95% is dark and invisible, similarly, most of the suffering is invisible.

You see the visible suffering in hospitals, courtrooms, shelters, and more. The invisible suffering is everywhere—in offices, cafeterias, malls, kitchens, bedrooms, and basements.

This realization has helped my relationships tremendously. I assume and try my best to remember that everyone I meet is struggling. This realization helps me be kind, even on days when every traffic light turns red for me right as I am approaching the intersection.
Think of someone today who seems very strong and looks like he is having a great time. Now, think of a few ways this person may be struggling.

When you meet that person the next time, remember that he has many invisible struggles. It will help you be kind.
Keeping that awareness throughout the day for everyone might bring out your best in your every interpersonal connection.

Day 150

It's easy to be kind to influential and important people. True kindness is being kind to those who depend on you.

Let me tell you about a particularly annoying colleague.

In her tirade to deliver the numbers that the leadership wanted, she cared little about the struggles of the junior staff. A constant schemer, she was very popular with the leaders but silently despised by those she supervised.

With a big ego and small heart, when one of her colleagues developed a test for early cancer diagnosis, without thinking about its value to the patients, she would go mad if someone ordered that test. Why did she do that?

Because the colleague who developed the test was junior to her and in her mind, didn't give her enough credit.

Some researchers call this the slime effect—kind to seniors, nasty to juniors. I find these people even more annoying than those who are predictably nasty to everyone. Because the universally nasty people likely have a genetic predisposition to nastiness. The slime effect is largely intentional.

I must say, though, that almost every one of us has a touch of slime effect. I recognize its presence within me. Whenever I have given a little extra attention to someone influential and less attention to someone who is less resourceful, I have practiced the slime effect.

This recognition is empowering because it helps me intentionally try my best to be kind to those who depend on me. I am sure I fail at it at times but trying is better than not trying.

So, think of different ways you can be kind to someone who depends on you.

I believe life is an echo—the good you send comes back to you. When you are good to someone who depends on you, that good will return to you, particularly on a day you need it the most.

Thank you for being good and kind today.

Day 151

Empty the space in your brain taken by self-doubt. Replace it with hope, inspiration, and courage.

Restaurant menus have been around since the 18th century. And they have been increasing in length. The longest menu recorded so far has more than 1800 items.

But even with a menu that is a thousand items long, how many would you order for your 2.5-ounce stomach? Two, maybe three, right?

The same is true about your brain. While billions of bytes of data strike your sensory system at any moment, your brain can only process a hundred bytes or so at a point in time.

Just as your dinner experience depends not on the items in the menu but what's on your plate, similarly, your present moment experience

depends not on the totality of the input but what your brain internalizes and experiences at this moment.

In our default operation, though, the brain internalizes the negative much more than the positive. For some reason, the language of fear and self-doubt seems more valuable and believable. This instinct short-changes us. It depletes our resilience every single day.

Take charge today and replace self-doubt with hope, inspiration, and courage. Engage in a self-dialogue that fills you with energy, helps you be your best self, and creates a tomorrow of your choosing.

As a first step, let's think of a few good reasons to feel hopeful, inspired, and courageous today.

Once you convince your mind that your brain's default operation needs to be (and can be) tweaked, you'll take charge, and create a mindset guided by your values and not the ancestral struggles that have shaped our neural system over generations.

Day 152

Replace fear with hope. Support hope with courage. Direct courage toward meaning.

Before the invention of the clock and the compass, sailors relied on Polaris, also called the North Star, to help them with directions. It was simple: face Polaris to face north; with Polaris on your back, you are facing south.

When thinking about our life's purpose, it helps to think about the North Star—the shining light that guides your life. Here are three questions that might help open your eyes to this light.

1. What is more precious to me than my dear life?

2. How can I use my strengths and skills to help build a better world?

3. What unites me with other fellow human beings?

Pause and think today about these questions.

The answers to all three questions point you to your values, purpose, passions, strength, and identity.

Greater clarity about your purpose will help you put effort and courage to meet that purpose while living with your values and keeping the hope that your efforts will bring fruit.

I think, given all our constraints, that's an excellent first step to start living with greater meaning.

The people and purpose you serve indeed power your efforts.

Day 153

The light is one, the candles many. More the candles, brighter the light.

As the night falls, trillions of candles, lamps, bulbs, and flashlights illuminate our world. Even tiny glow worms do their job in lighting a small dark corner behind a bush.

All the lights harness the power from one source—our sun—and recreate light in different colors and patterns.

While the candles, lamps, bulbs, and flashlights look different, they all have one thing in common—they spread the energy they received from elsewhere.

Similarly, you are bringing light to the world in your unique way. While the particular hue and pattern may be different from someone else, every person is harnessing the wisdom and love from its source and sharing it back with the world.

You may be running a daycare, a laundromat, flying an airplane, plowing snow on the road, or running a company. Doesn't matter. While the means are different, the meaning is the same—each person is an agent of service and love.

Friend, we all are different shades of the same light. The deeper you look, the clearer you'll see that we are all closely connected.

Don't you think this thought is enough for us to be a little bit more generous about sharing our gift of kind presence in this tiny little corner of the world? I think it is.

Even though the candles are many, it helps to believe and know that the light indeed is one.

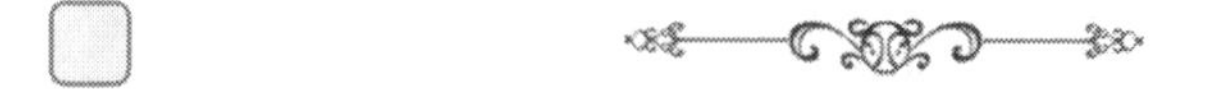

Day 154

Here are the six key ideas we learned this week. Pick the one that makes the most sense to you for today.

- ☐ *Try your best not to quit. But if you feel spent, nothing wrong with taking a break.*

- ☐ *Recognize that majority of suffering in the world is invisible. This recognition might help you default to kindness.*

- ☐ *It's easy to be kind to influential and important people. True kindness is being kind to those who depend on you. When you are good to someone who depends on you, that good will return to you, particularly on a day you need it the most.*

- ☐ *Empty the space in your brain taken by self-doubt. Replace it with hope, inspiration, and courage. As a first step, think of a few good reasons to feel hopeful, inspired, and courageous today.*

- ☐ *Replace fear with hope. Support hope with courage. Direct courage toward meaning. The people and purpose you serve indeed power your efforts.*

- ☐ *The light is one, the candles many. More the candles, brighter the light. Share with universal compassion your gift of kind presence in this tiny little corner of the world. Be generous in your sharing.*

I pray you find hope and healing today.

WEEKS 23-24

Theme: Help those facing the pain you had to endure
Inspiring figure: Harriet Tubman

Harriet spent most of her childhood in hardships, enduring emotional and physical abuse. In 1849, after she escaped from slavery, Tubman organized an "underground railroad" that freed over three hundred slaves. No wonder she was called the "Moses." She even led an armed expedition that freed over 700 slaves. After the Civil War, she spent the rest of her life helping former slaves and the elderly.

Here are two of Tubman's most inspiring quotes:

"Every great dream begins with a dreamer. Always remember, you have within you the strength, the patience, and the passion to reach for the stars to change the world."

"I had reasoned this out in my mind; there was one of two things I had a right to, liberty or death; if I could not have one, I would have the other; for no man should take me alive."

Day 155

Showing that you care can reverse the effect of stress on people's brains. You can't lift their load, but your care can help them find greater strength.

Hippocampus is a sea horse-shaped brain structure that is critical for memory. Consider it the ringmaster of the memory orchestra.

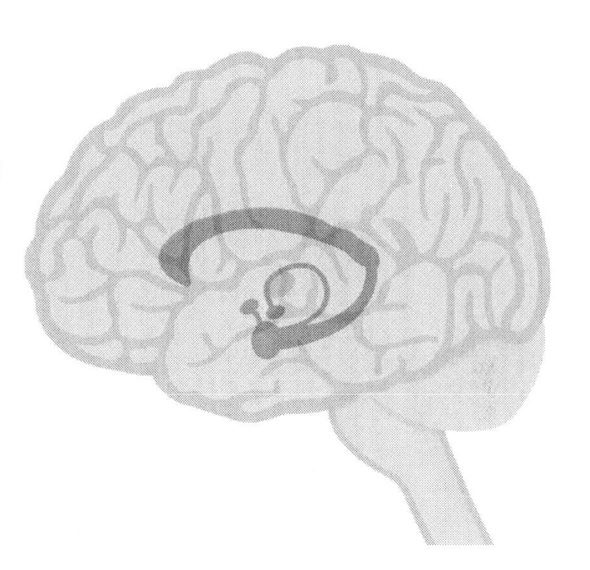

Neurological conditions associated with atrophy or loss of the hippocampus universally cause memory loss.

Interestingly, the hippocampus is one part of the brain that constantly generates new neurons. This process needs energy and nutrients. Many conditions thus affect hippocampal integrity. Malnutrition and chronic stress are two of them. They are connected by one common factor—poverty.

Research shows that poverty has a devastating effect on the hippocampus by slowing its ability to generate new neurons. This damage interferes with memory and intellect, decreasing one's ability to succeed.

The resulting trap perpetuates the cycle of poverty.

But here is a reason for hope. Research shows that kind and engaged parenting can completely reverse the damaging effect of poverty on the hippocampus. Also, the benefit isn't limited to just parenting but to kindness from anyone.

Perhaps you can see the connection. Think about the people you know who came from a very modest background but grew up very successful. Very likely, their lives were touched by someone kind and inspiring.

That's the kindness Harriet Tubman showed as she worked tirelessly to lift countless lives.

Think today of how you can help compensate for someone's struggles by bringing greater kindness to that person's life.

Day 156

You only truly receive and experience the love you believe you deserve.

When you walk on a fully paved road, you barely leave any mark. But if you manage to walk on freshly poured concrete, you will leave deep dents. And an angry contractor.

Children's brains are like freshly poured concrete. Scratching them can leave long-lasting scars. And if that scratching is repeated and occurs on a genetically vulnerable brain, then those brains lose the ability for self-love.

They get very skilled at self-loathing, become vulnerable to imposter syndrome—where they discount all that is good about them, considering their success as undeserved.

I know many people who struggle with this unhappy combination.

Ask yourself: What do I believe more—the compliments or the negative comments?

If it's the latter, perhaps you are struggling with a little bit of imposter syndrome. And you aren't alone. Three out of four among us experience some level of imposter syndrome.

Let's try to overcome it by taking control of our attention.

Instead of letting the bad dominate the good, let the good dilute the not-so-good. You can make that happen by focusing more of your attention on the good.

Today, take note of some of the compliments you have received that you fully deserved.

In fact, it's fair to consider that every compliment you have received you have fully deserved. Not believing this is shortchanging yourself and also the wisdom and effort of others who complimented you.

So, you have a choice in who to believe. Why not believe in those who believe in you—at least for today?

Day 157

The good people in your life are happy in your happiness; you can talk to them at 2 a.m. to share a worry.

When I sleep with an unresolved worry, I often wake up at 2 a.m. with that worry supersized. I catastrophize, think about the worst-case scenario.

Every negative, irrational thought seems completely believable at 2 in the morning. At that time, I can't rely on my mind's objectivity.

That's when I need my 2 a.m. people—those who I can call at an awkward hour not worried they will be judgmental of me.

I have seldom made that phone call. But it helps to do this thought experiment—think about who all you can call at 2 a.m. to share a worry. That list is precious, and for most of us, includes only a few people.

Likely, these are kind and wise people who trust and love you unconditionally. They are also happy in your happiness. They are the salt of the earth.

Pause your reading for a moment and think about who belongs to your 2 a.m. list?

Try and connect with at least one person on that list every week—to share challenges, successes, or just talk.

Talking to these people will remind you about what's good in this world.

And the more you feel you live in a good world, the better your world will become, putting you and the world in an upward spiral of life.

Day 158

You can't fail if you make a good-faith effort. Success is mostly about trying and not as much about winning.

I sometimes wonder what stories corporate executives who work for companies producing products that spoil our children's brains would be telling their grandchildren.

"I made lots of money by destroying the brain of a million teenagers."

Or, "I helped cause chronic lung disease in ten million children before they even got to college. By the way, son, this money will pay for your college tuition."

We are running on two converging tracks throughout our life's journey—what we are gaining and who we are becoming. Both are important, but I believe between the two, the second is more important.

If, in the process of gaining material wealth, fame, and success, we become self-centered, arrogant, and dishonest, and hurt a lot of people, then we didn't gain much at all.

I believe the world will be a much better place if we all focus more on who we are becoming as a person and less on how we are profiting.

Also, success is more about a good faith effort and honest intentions and less about the eventual outcome. Many people who were rejected by their world at the time, we now adore and revere.

So, keep your efforts and intentions pure today and let your honest hard work define your success.

If we all did that, I have no doubt we will collectively succeed by gaining what we aspire and becoming the person we admire.

Day 159

Let go of the uncontrollable. Focus most of your energy on problems that are important, actionable, and time sensitive.

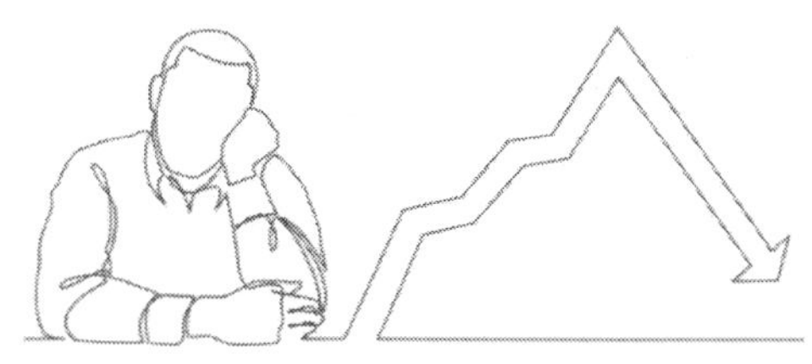

Let's say if someone was to ration your worries—you only get to worry a hundred times in a year. No more.

Won't you then prioritize and focus your worries on solvable problems that are within your control?

If you assume that the rationing is indeed real, then you'll let someone else think about the solar flares or what's happening on the other side of the moon and focus more on what's important and actionable.

You'll also save your energy by not trying to perfect the trivial—in yourself as well as others.

For example, accept for today that your partner loads the dishwasher like a garbage can while you prefer it looks like a jewelry box!

When trying to fix or worry about something, it helps to ask, is the cost worth the benefit? If not, then best to let go.

Bypassing the trivial and the unsolvable preserves your energy for the important and actionable.

So, today think about and commit to accept, some undesirable but uncontrollable aspects of your life that you are willing to accept. Acceptance doesn't mean it is right. All it means is you, as a wise person, do not pick challenges that aren't worth your time.

I hope you don't have to face too many challenges today.

Day 160

When you get busy helping the world, the world gets busy helping you. The world, however, is almost always slower than desired.

In the busy city traffic, truckers prefer to avoid the left lane. One of the most annoying experiences for truckers is people joining the lane ahead of them. Perhaps, you have done that at some point, as I have.

Why do we do that? Because truckers drive the slowest in the city. And for a good reason. The bigger the vehicle, the longer it takes to accelerate and decelerate. The same applies to the world.

If you feel like all your years of sincere efforts remain unnoticed, the reason is simple—the world is slow to notice and respond to your goodness. The world also falls in love with you slowly. Expecting the world to operate at your speed and efficiency is a setup for disappointment.

But keep the faith and your patience. Keep doing good for the world because, the surest way to succeed is to help others succeed.

I don't know specifically how it works at an energetic or cosmic level, but learning from my life and observing others, I am convinced that one of the best ways to help myself is to help the world.

So, consider forgiving and accepting situations where your good actions were neither recognized nor reciprocated. They will eventually be valued, and the rewards will be more than you ever anticipated.

Just keep the patience. Lift the load of only today's disappointments. Tomorrow's sunrise will bring fresh hope and fresh possibilities.

Day 161

Here are the six key ideas we learned this week. Pick the one that makes the most sense to you for today.

- ☐ *Showing that you care can reverse the effect of stress on people's brains. You can't lift their load, but your care can help them find greater strength. Think today of how you can help compensate for someone's struggles by bringing greater kindness to that person's life.*

- ☐ *You only truly receive and experience the love you believe you deserve. Believe in those who believe in you—at least for today.*

- ☐ *The good people in your life are happy in your happiness; you can talk to them at 2 a.m. to share a worry. Try and connect with at least one person today who loves you unconditionally and accepts you just as you are.*

- ☐ *You can't fail if you make a good-faith effort. Success is mostly about trying and not as much about winning. Keep your efforts and intentions pure today, and let your honest hard work define your success.*

- ☐ *Let go of the uncontrollable. Focus most of your energy on problems that are important, actionable, and time-sensitive. Think about and commit to accept some undesirable but uncontrollable aspects of your life that you are willing to accept, if only for today.*

- ☐ *When you get busy helping the world, the world gets busy helping you. The world, however, is almost always slower than desired. Just be a little extra patient. If feasible, lift the load of only the next 24 hours, even better only the next hour.*

I pray you find hope and healing today.

Day 162

Research shows living your days with a strong sense of purpose can decrease the risk of heart attack by as much as 25 percent.

Here is a helpful summary of wellbeing and happiness research—when you tell your physical body that I am having a good time on this planet, and I am needed here, your genes and immune system start preparing for the long haul. Inflammation goes down, anti-viral immunity improves.

On the other hand, if you tell your genes that I am not having a good time and am not fulfilling a purpose, your genes and immune system start preparing for a quicker exit by increasing inflammation. Your blood starts clotting quicker, and your anti-viral immunity goes down.

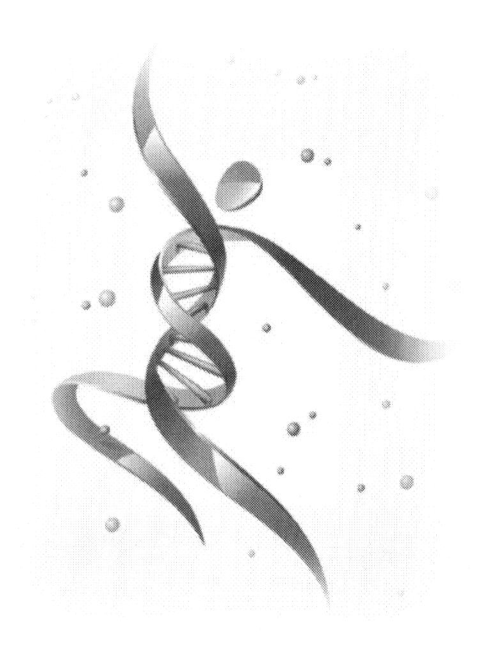

This is very similar to going to a party. You stay longer at a party that you are enjoying. You also stay longer if you are the DJ or responsible for the food.

No wonder research on meaning shows that when you live your days with a strong sense of purpose, your heart health improves, and you live longer.

Often, the meaning doesn't have to be invented. It's already there and is waiting to be discovered.

Think of the deeper meaning behind your personal and professional life. This meaning can be captured in four words—building, becoming, belonging, and believing.

Building a company, a product, or a similar entity. Becoming a successful entrepreneur, teacher, nurse, university professor, or some other such role. Belonging to a family, a circle of friends, or another group. Believing in faith, nature, or another pious entity.

Reflect on these four words—Building, Becoming, Belonging, and Believing. Think about the aspect of life in which you are most underperforming. And then, take the first step to grow in that domain.

It might help decrease your inflammation and improve your overall health.

Day 163

The commonest cause of heart failure isn't the heart's inability to squeeze; it is its inability to relax.

For the longest time, cardiologists believed the most common cause of heart failure was its inability to squeeze. But now we know that isn't the case. The most typical cause isn't a weakness in the squeeze; it is its inability to relax (technically called diastolic dysfunction).

A stiff heart cannot receive the blood as efficiently as a supple heart, impairing its function.

I think the same applies to the mind. A stiff mind that can't relax struggles with receiving the goodness the world sends to us. Such a mind struggles with self-love and self-acceptance, which morphs into arrogance, anger, misguided pursuits, and more.

A relaxed mind is content and kind. Relaxation doesn't lead to inaction. It leads to positive action where one thinks, speaks, and acts to help the world while fulfilling personal responsibilities.

Doing the right thing, feeling grateful, cultivating kindness, remaining humble, forgiving the self and others, keeping the hope, finding courage, meditating, praying, and nurturing faith—are different ways to feel relaxed.

Pick one or more ideas from the above list and think of additional ideas, so you feel more relaxed today.

☐ 

Day 164

The good people are very good at feeling bad about themselves. If you have felt bad about yourself, it's a proof that you are a good person.

Let me ask you this question that I may have asked thousands of times. "Do you struggle with being appreciated too much?"

I have seldom had anyone respond yes to that question. Most of us, even those who are pampered daily, struggle with self-worth. Why is that?

It is because our mind acts like a sieve that lets the positives pass unattended but collects the debris of negativity. If not cleared, this debris clogs the mind and influences the present-moment experience.

Feeling bad about yourself is not necessarily bad. It means your moral compass is alive and kicking. But it comes at a cost—you shortchange yourself in the process.

I think an optimal combination is to experience both a mix of good and not-so-good. Recognize your strengths and goodness while also knowing well the areas you are working on. To me, that is humility.

But given that many of us struggle with self-worth, a good idea today is to write a few reasons those who think you are a good person are correct in their assumption.

The purpose isn't to boast about your goodness. It is to feel worthy and use your energy to continue rising in your life's journey.

Day 165

Courage keeps the company of humility. You'll often hear the courageous say, "I was just doing my job."

A person jumps off the bridge to save a drowning child. Another person jumps in front of an oncoming train to save a man stuck on the railroad track. A young boy runs into a burning house to save his little sister. These are all true heroic stories of tremendous courage.

But when you ask these people later about their exceptional courage, they commonly say, "I was just doing the right thing. Anyone in my place would have done just that."

Authentic courage keeps the company of humility, wisdom, and altruism. The courageous don't jump into the lion enclosure at the zoo just for the thrill of it.

Courage thus isn't the absence of fear. Courage is doing the right thing despite the fear. Courage draws strength from purpose and hope. The more hopeful you feel and the more profound your meaning, the greater your courage. Courage also finds its strength from social connections, believing in oneself, having good role models, and faith.

So, think about the most courageous people in your life and what gives them their strength. Live your day with greater courage, remembering these wonderful people.

Day 166

Your genes are important, but they aren't your destiny. A more powerful influencer of your future is your strong will guided by your wisdom.

Happiness, resilience, wellbeing, patience, hope—they are all about 50% genetic and 50% related to your behaviors and lifestyle.

While you can't choose the genes you are born with, at least not yet, you can influence which genes express themselves. And that's enough to change your life's course.

If that weren't the case, we would have no power to improve our stamina, bulk up our muscles, or empower our immune system.

Interestingly though, attributes that are genetically determined and evolutionarily imprinted need constant effort to maintain the change.

So, if you have naturally curly hair and straighten them, your hair will again start showing the waves after a few days. You have to keep straightening your hair to maintain the change. That's where intentionality comes.

If you have a biological predisposition towards sadness or anxiety, life's stressors are likely to have an outsized impact on you.

The good news is that you can undo a large part of the stress by choosing a different thinking pattern. When repeated over a period of time, these thoughts carve a very different brain compared to what your genes would have given you.

Clearly, your strong will guided by your wisdom is very powerful.

Write today one of your limitations you have overcome in the previous years and what that experience has taught you about yourself and life. This little practice might help you feel empowered. It might help you believe that you can overcome your genetic predisposition.

You are stronger and more gifted than you know or can ever know. Just take my word for it.

Day 167

When the present moment is challenged, zoom out. When the long term is challenged, zoom in.

Think about a gazelle being chased by a lion. The lion gets distracted and gazelle escapes. What do you think the little animal would be doing a few minutes later?

Most likely munching on grass, sipping some water, and hanging out with buddies.

Now think about a human being chased by a lion. The human escapes. What do you think he would be dealing with a few minutes later? Likely, he would be having a panic attack, might develop PTSD, and need therapy for life.

Do you see how we are so much more emotionally vulnerable compared to other animals?

Our excellent memory and imagination ability keep us close to our hurts. And imagination is reality.

If we leave our brain to its default, then it keeps our attention glued to the threatening. Luckily, we have intentionality. We can focus our attention on what is most nurturing. That's where zoom in and zoom out, or Zizo comes.

Zoom in and live your life, picking the load of only the next hour if the intermediate or long-term is challenged. For example, if I am getting a colonoscopy next week, and it's Friday evening, then I want to zoom in to have a good time over the weekend.

Zoom out and think of the long-term if the present moment is challenged. For example, while sitting on the dentist's chair and getting a procedure, plan something interesting next week.

Leverage your brain's capacity to switch your attention.

Place your attention at a place or experience that gives you calm—whether in this moment or something you look forward to in the coming months and years.

This isn't escaping from life or reality. It is diluting the unpleasant with the pleasant so you can preserve your sanity and keep living the best you can.

Day 168

Here are the six key ideas we learned this week. Pick the one that makes the most sense to you for today.

- [ ] *Research shows living your days with a strong sense of purpose can decrease the risk of heart attack by as much as 25 percent. Reflect on these four words to think about your meaning—Building, Becoming, Belonging, and Believing. Think about the aspect of life in which you are most underperforming. And take the first step to grow in that domain.*

- [ ] *The most common cause of heart failure isn't the heart's inability to squeeze; it is its inability to relax. Pick one or more ideas from this list to feel more relaxed today: Do the right thing, feel grateful, cultivate kindness, remain humble, forgive the self and others, keep the hope, find courage, meditate, pray, and nurture faith.*

- [ ] *The good people are very good at feeling bad about themselves. If you have felt bad about yourself, it's a proof that you are a good person. Consider writing a few reasons those who think you are a good person are correct in their assumption. The purpose of this isn't to boast about your goodness. It is to feel worthy and use your energy to continue rising in your life's journey.*

- [ ] *Courage keeps the company of humility. You'll often hear the courageous say, "I was just doing my job." Think about the most courageous people in your life and what gives them their strength. That awareness will increase your own courage.*

- [ ] *Your genes are important, but they aren't your destiny. A more powerful influencer of your future is your strong will guided by your wisdom. Write a few of your limitations you have overcome in the previous years and what that experience has taught you about yourself and life. You are stronger and more gifted than you know or can ever know.*

- [ ] *When the present moment is challenged, zoom out. When the long term is challenged, zoom in. This isn't escaping from life or reality. It is diluting the unpleasant with the pleasant so you can preserve your sanity and keep living the best you can.*

I pray you find hope and healing today.

Acknowledgements

I am grateful to my parents (Sahib and Shashi), brother (Kishore), sisters (Sandhya and Rajni), daughters (Gauri and Sia), and my lovely wife (Richa). My gratitude to my friends, teachers, other relatives, colleagues, neighbors, patients, and clients. I am also thankful to my newest teacher in wisdom and love, our adorable goldendoodle Simba.

Additional Resources by Dr. Sood

Websites: resilientoption.com

Resiliencetrainer.com

happigenius.com

Books: *SMART with Dr. Sood*

Mayo Clinic Guide to Stress-Free Living

Mayo Clinic Handbook for Happiness

The Resilience Journal

Stronger: The Science and Art of Stress Resilience

Mindfulness Redesigned for the 21st Century

Build Your Immune Resilience

2021: Your Year of Healing

Mobile Apps: Zizo: Your Personal Resilience Assistant

HappiGenius

About the Author

Dr. Amit Sood is married to his lovely wife of 28 years, Dr. Richa Sood. They have two daughters, Gauri (age 17) and Sia (age 10).

Dr. Sood is the Executive Director of the Global Center for Resiliency and Wellbeing and The GRIT Institute. He is internationally known for his work on stress management, resilience, wellbeing, mindfulness, and burnout.

He is a former Professor of Medicine at Mayo Clinic, director of the Mind-Body Medicine Initiative, and *Carla J Paonessa* enterprise chair of student life and wellbeing.

Dr. Sood completed his medical school at Gandhi Medical College, Bhopal, residencies in internal medicine at the All India Institute of Medical Sciences (AIIMS), New Delhi, and Albert Einstein School of Medicine, New York, an integrative medicine fellowship at the University of Arizona and earned a master's degree in clinical research from Mayo Clinic College of Medicine. He has received several National Institutes of Health grants and foundation awards to test and implement integrative and mind-body approaches within medicine.

Dr. Sood's work has resulted in many resilience and wellbeing programs including Resilient Option, Stress Management and Resiliency Training (SMART©), Certified Resilience Trainer (CeRT) Course, HappiGenius, and Zizo: Your Resilience Assistant. The programs have been adopted by several hospitals, health systems, and corporate as their resiliency and wellbeing platform.

SMART has been tested in over thirty clinical trials and reaches approximately 250,000 participants each year. It is beneficial for a broad demographic, including corporate executives, health care professionals, patients, caregivers, educators, parents, and students.

Dr. Sood has authored or co-authored over 80 peer-reviewed articles, and additionally, editorials, book chapters, abstracts, and letters. He has also authored multiple books, including *The Mayo Clinic Guide to Stress-Free Living, The Mayo Clinic Handbook for Happiness, Immerse: A 52-Week Course in Resilient Living, Mindfulness Redesigned for the Twenty-First Century, Stronger, SMART with Dr. Sood,* and *2021: Your Year of Healing.*

As an international expert in his field, Dr. Sood's work has been widely cited in the press, including *The Atlantic Monthly, USA Today, Wall Street Journal, New York Times, Forbes, NPR, Reuters Health, Time Magazine (online), Good Housekeeping, Parenting, Real Simple, Shape, US News, Huffington Post, Mens Health Magazine, AARP, The Globe and Mail, Fox News,* and *CBS News.* He is highly sought after as a speaker on resilience and stress management, presenting more than 100 workshops each year. Dr. Sood's videos, including the TEDx talk, *Happy Brain: How to Overcome Our Neural Predispositions to Suffering,* and *A Very Happy Brain,* have been seen by millions of viewers all over the world.

Dr. Sood received the 2010 Distinguished Service Award, the 2010 Innovator of the Year Award, the 2013 Outstanding Physician Scientist Award, and the 2016 Faculty of the Year Award from Mayo Clinic. He also was honored as the Robert Wood Johnson Health Care Pioneer in 2015. *The Intelligent Optimist* (formerly *Ode Magazine*) selected Dr. Sood as one of the top 20 intelligent optimists helping the world be a better place. In 2016, Dr. Sood was selected as the top impact maker in healthcare in Rochester, MN.

Dr. Sood serves on the wellbeing advisory board for Everyday Health and the Scientific advisory board for BetterUp.

Made in the USA
Las Vegas, NV
04 March 2023